ALMOST AN ISLAND

Edited by Ian Moir

For copyright of individual contributions, see page vii.

First published in 2010 via lulu.com.

Created by Dunfermline Arts and Media (www.thedam.org.uk).

Edited by Ian Moir. Assistant editors: Ross Wilson, Keith Mitchell.

Typeset by Dominic Franey (www.dghf.co.uk).

ISBN 978-1-4457-3125-4

PREFACE

GEOGRAPHICALLY, Fife is almost an island but culturally it is completely so. I doubt if there is a Scot alive who would deny that. This fact is supported by several amusing road signs which remind us upon entering and leaving the region that Fife is indeed a separate 'kingdom'. We, the editing team, were looking to investigate the influence of this cultural autonomy on the literary community, if indeed such a community existed, and bring it to the fore by way of an anthology. We stuck rigorously to the principle that wherever there are people, there is art. Ultimately, we were not disappointed.

In the submissions brief we stipulated that the contributors needed to be either living in Fife or be connected to the region by birth, upbringing or education. We were careful not to inadvertently prescribe local subjects (e.g., coal mining, fishing, football!) lest we summon an overt parochialism that would be hard to bear. Nor did we wish to limit anyone in their creative choices. Truthfulness, authenticity and excellence were our only requirements, so no theme was ever proposed.

Our selection process was thorough, each submission being considered by three editors. We insisted upon a high level of craftsmanship but tried also to create space for previously unpublished writers. To our delight, the standard was generally high and those whose work has not been included should take heart, they gave us difficult choices to make.

I would like to thank Iain Cranford Hunter for allowing us to use his drawings in this publication. Their economy of line and dark wit could, I fancy, only ever have come from a Fifer. I would also like to thank Ross Wilson and Keith Mitchell for their hard work and commitment to the project. Thank you, finally, to all the writers and poets for their submissions. I trust this anthology will further cement

Fife's place in the literary establishment.

— Ian Moir, November 2009

ACKNOWLEDGEMENTS

'Giants', 'Sunday Wakes' copyright © Glenn Gates 2009.

'Fife, Texas' copyright © Daniel Kalder 2009.

'Queen of the Haugh', 'Cicadas & Lisa', 'The Auspica are Dumb', 'A Woman is Drowning', 'The Water Must Have Risen Imperceptibly', 'I Have Stared upon the Snow', 'On Battling Tides', 'Extricate', 'We Have the Lakeside Park All to Ourselves', 'Seascape', 'Dirge' copyright © Robert Stark 2009.

'Caught Short in Mid Calder; copyright © Iain Bahlaj 2009.

'The Abbey Walk' copyright © Ross Wilson 2009. 'The Way John Went Out' copyright © Ross Wilson 2007.

'The Auld Grey Toun' copyright © Gifford Lind 1996. 'Across the Scotswater' copyright © Gifford Lind 2003. 'The Coal Dust Still Moves in the Sand' copyright © Gifford Lind 2004. 'Waiting for the Calm' copyright © Gifford Lind 1997. 'Cross of Lorraine' copyright © Gifford Lind 1995.

'Skint', 'Singing For My Supper' copyright © Elaine Renton 2009.

'Concrete Echoes' copyright © Greg Whelan 2009.

'Greenland' excerpted from *True North – Travels in Arctic Europe* copyright © Gavin Francis 2008.

'Peal Loud and Clear, Dunfermline Bells!', 'Still the Rain Buckets Down on Coal Yard Lane', 'The Likes of John Higgs' copyright © David Seagrave 2009.

'Abstractions From Along Another Way' copyright © John Mingay 2009.

'The Silent Scream' copyright © Derek Fyfe 2009.

'Funeral (in memory of Jim Braid)' copyright © Sean Howie 2009.

'When the Women Disappeared' copyright © Rachel Marsh 2009.

'Servant', 'Doubleganger', 'Advent', 'May-day Ascension', 'Forward', 'A Poem about Gardening', 'Climbing Through Windows' copy-

THANKS

Almost an Island is supported by:

CONTENTS

Fiction

Poems

Travel Writing

Songs

Artwork

(All artworks by Iain Crawford Hunter)

After the break-up

04 10 03
After the
break-up.

GLENN GATES

GIANTS

Over the firth in the gloaming I saw rainbows,
Three of them at far intervals
Broad in shoulder – more stump than bow,
Silver haired giants in bright robes
Trampling a wealth of crystal.

Before that I saw a jakey punch another jakey in the face.

SUNDAY WAKES

THE LOVE handles are gone, leaving the skin sore to grasp. In the darkened bedroom, my running clothes are draped over the bed end. I come out of sleep with talk radio keenly discussing sport, and I become aware of narrative thinking in my head. I arise, wondering if I've always done this in the mornings, put some coffee on to brew, open a crack in the curtains and blow on my cold hands before typing. Moisture runs down the steamy windows. The coffee aroma hits from the kitchen and Sunday begins. It is almost one o'clock.

The first cup is gone in seconds, my body is trying to rehydrate after last night's beer. I must force down some water, sometimes three pints can cause a hangover when you're 47, but that can be blamed most times on closing time hunger and the rubbish you devoured.

I'd gone out late on Saturday night, alone. I determined to be interested in observing other people, to be open minded and see the persons under their social persona. Observe and learn, be interested in humanity. But I kept seeing them in terms of potential for characters in a novel. All I could see were background artistes in a heaving provincial nightspot. Stock characters such as 'overexcited dancing boy' whose flailing arms upset drinks and smack passers-by on the tits.

Naturally each figure in the crowd has its own dramas to tell of, the human story in microcosm, each connecting to the great whole. Is there life before death? Do they believe in a creator with a human face, or in a more Taoist model of the universe? On a Saturday night, are those the questions they'd be asking? Men want to get laid, women want to feel the security of being desired – they might pretend not to like it, but it matters plenty. Some of the more confident women just want laid too, but oftentimes it's drink, not confidence.

It's obvious who the lead man is in this piece, I look for my supporting cast, perhaps a worthy nemesis or other uninvited sparring partner, or a well-read drunk. There is no leading lady on this set, mere floozies with twisted cussing mouths. There is a kind of glamour in the air, the sort that shop and factory girls project in their club clothes, which, in our times, usually means plenty naked flesh. If she has an iffy face but half decent legs, she wears the shortest skirt possible. On the video monitors a legendary female pop singer is greased up in a leather thong. She waves her arse in our faces and strokes herself all over, surrounded by near naked dancers who, with sluttish theatricality, pretend to be lesbians. Sex is power. I don't watch pop videos in normal life, that's why I missed noticing who the female role models of today are, and why grass roots female drinkers act the way they do. In my minds eye, I see ambitious young flesh sat astride the totemic poles of record bosses.

A female in her thirties who dresses like a teenager, catches my eye from her nearby seat. I look back with a polite smile. Just to let her know who's boss without seeming unfriendly. Her companion sitting with her back to me, turns around, she has that sour peasanty face that is considered attractive among the regular locals. I reflect her cold hostility and she tries to stare me down. I look back to her companion with a polite quizzical smile, then back to the sour chick with impassive face. She looks back at me several times until I show my sense of tedium, raising eyes upwards and away, refusing to indulge her sullen-mouthed attention-whoring any longer.

An extended arm reaches towards me and I examine it like some careless person left a curious fish on the seat beside me. Slightly offended at my lack of compliance in friendly bonding with a drunk stranger, his welcoming hand becomes the one fingered salute.

— I've spoken to you before, he announces.

I nod absently.

— I'm always telling you to fucking smile

— Now I remember

Forced jollity and drunk people, I know this tale. True to form he demands I relax.

— I am relaxed

— I'd hate to see you uptight

— Have you got a sore back?

— Not yet

I already know he refers to my habitually upright posture, and I don't take the bait. Classy chicks like it, the rest don't.

— Tak your jaiket aff [trans.: *Take your jacket off*]

If you like a certain kind of story, there are excellent authors who deal in earthy provincials and do so with brilliance. But I live in that world, or at least on the very edge of it. When it comes down to it, the themes are eternal and cross all social boundaries, they're about feeling, compassion, humanity, love, death, hate, theft, war, revenge, comedy, tragedy and I can enjoy earthy writers as much as you can. But like fun, I don't need it shoved down my throat.

— I like wearing it

The jazzy handkerchief crammed with mock carelessness into the top pocket of this pinstripe lounge jacket tells of a different era. It's ironic that you can stand out in a crowd by dressing with a sly traditional edge.

— You'll not get fixed unless you tak it aff and relax [trans.: *you won't get sex*]

— If I see anything among those I actually fancy, maybe I'll take your advice

— How old are you?

— Fifty-four

— Don't take the pish [trans.: *I don't believe you*]

I am non-reactive and he begins to believe me.

— Well there's older birds here as well. And loads of women keep looking at you mate.

— I've spoken to loads of them here in the past, they're not very friendly

— That's because you're a dick

There is a lot to be said for plain-speaking people. If we had anything to talk about and I was drunk too, he'd be good company if I were in the right mood. It's Saturday night, it isn't meant to be an anthropology class. I observe and I learn, I can't help it. I'd love it if an elegantly dressed anthropologist woman sat on my lap. Can't say I've met any such thing round these parts. On the face of things, it was a mistake to leave the city and return to the province, but circumstances made it seem the best choice at the time. I love choices.

There is only one show in this town.

Honeymoon

honeymoon

10 06 03

DANIEL KALDER

FIFE, TEXAS

THERE ARE thousands of ghost towns in Texas, settlements that were planted in hope but which never took root, that ran out of reasons to exist first, people second, and only then died – usually after a long and protracted struggle with their own pointlessness. Recently I've been exploring these phantoms, drawn in by the combination of oblivion and mystery like a liver fluke to a particularly appealing bile duct. There's a challenge there, in the sand and in the dust. Yes, it looks like nothing, but it's only apparently nothing. There are still traces, echoes, whispers of a past life hanging in the heat, or concealed in the dirt and scrub. You just need to look hard enough.

With so many ghost towns to choose from, it can be difficult to select a candidate for exploration. You can study maps of course, or get a guide book like T. Lindsey Baker's excellent *Ghost Towns of Texas.* Sometimes you pass them by chance, in the car, although if so there's a strong possibility you won't notice, as a true ghost town will have little to show for itself. Alternatively you can get avant-garde and adopt nonsensical methods of divination. I like to feed nouns into Google Maps and see if there's a town in Texas bearing that name. That's how I discovered Art, Earth, Eden, Paradise and even Tarzan. But some of those towns are still alive, interesting enough but offering different pleasures from a ghost settlement. I tried Dunfermline, my hometown in Scotland to see if it had a parallel in Texas, but without luck. Fife however – that was close by, in Llano County, just a few hours from Austin, where I live. It had been founded by colonists from the original, Scottish Fife in the late 19th century. Better yet, after just over a century of existence it was on the verge of total annihilation, if it had not already ceased to be completely.

An expedition was in my future.

I drove out of Austin, heading north on the freeway anticipating an epic voyage. By epic, of course, I mean a six-hour round trip in the car, with maybe fifteen minutes of walking around in Fife's emptiness, and a break for lunch in a nearby town – that's assuming I didn't make any wrong turnings. But I missed a road somewhere outside Lampasas and so soon I was sailing freely into the heart of Texas, past tiny settlements and ghost towns.

I passed Center City, which is intriguing because it is neither the centre of anything nor is it a city. In the 1870s, however, its founders thought that they had discovered the very geographical heart of Texas, which they believed was marked by a great oak tree they had found reaching up out of the earth. A whole town was built around a square which was left intentionally empty for the great courthouse which would one day be erected there, and from which a judge would dispense THE LAW. However it turned out that the town of Brady a few miles away was the actual heart of the state. Worse, Center City was not even granted the dignity of being the centre of its own county, and the long-awaited courthouse was erected in nearby Goldthwaite instead. Center City started to curl up and die around 1910. Not quite dead nearly a hundred years later, today a few houses and the tree remain, as a testament to questionable land surveying.

Then I passed through one of the Swedens – whether it was East or West Sweden I can't remember. These settlements were – surprise, surprise – founded by Swedes in the late 19th century. Both are now completely uninhabited, although curious traces of the life that used to exist remain. One Sweden contains a church which is still visited by the living, breathing descendants of the original settlers, while the other boasts a graveyard, teeming with the bones of the dead, who haunt the dirt.

Finally I hurtled past a sign for *Camp Billy Gibbons*. Now that was a discovery – a Boy Scout camp named after ZZ Top's guitarist! This was Texas surrealism of the highest order. A long road led beyond the horizon to a mysterious zone where strange, perhaps forbidden events unfolded every summer. What happened at the end of that road, I wondered? Did Gibbons teach young boys to read their Bibles and play their instruments, while encouraging them to nuzzle under his beard, like a hillbilly Michael Jackson? (In fact no: later I discovered it was named after another Billy Gibbons, with no connection at all to Texan blues rock).

By now however I had figured out how I had fallen off the edge of the map. A few turnings later and I was once more headed for Fife, via Brady – the true geographical heart of Texas, and thus of course the universe.

Brady is a town of a few thousand, caught in a state of mild dilapidation, like one of those prehistoric flies trapped in amber. And yet it enjoys a vigorous spiritual life. The benches on the town square bore plaques bearing citations from the New Testament. I had never seen this before, even in rural, religious Texas, where God is frequently to be found standing over your shoulder, breathing down your neck, reminding you that there is a Hell and it's full of sinners just like you. Rather than give you the actual text of the verse however the plaques merely teased you with Biblical coordinates. You'd have to do a little work yourself if you hoped for salvation. I took a photograph of one plaque, which encouraged me to read 1 Thessalonians 5:10. Later I did, and this is what it says:

> Who died for us, that, whether we wake or sleep, we should live together with him.

Admittedly without verse 9, which contains the first half of the sentence, it is rather confusing. Another plaque exhorted me to read John 3:16, which is more complete:

> For God so loved the world, that he gave his only begotten Son, that whosoever believeth in him should not perish, but have everlasting life.

What they both indicate however is that the people of Brady have their eyes fixed firmly on eternity; theirs is a truly cosmic viewpoint. Indeed, this was a whole other world, located a mere three hours from the godless metropolis of Austin – a 'nest of perverts' as one fiery Baptist preacher had described it to me shortly after my arrival in Texas. All the shops in Brady were closed and the town's handful of streets were abandoned because it was Good Friday, the day that marks Christ's crucifixion and death at Calvary, when no man of any decency should be engaged in profane business. I had forgotten, and now, walking about in Brady when everybody else was indoors contemplating the state of their immortal souls I suddenly felt like a no-good, dirty heathen. According to an announcement in the post-office window, the town would return to life in a day's time as its citizens celebrated Christ's resurrection Texas-style, with an evening of *Wrestling for Jesus* in the local school gymnasium.

Now that, surely, is the sort of muscular Christianity we all can admire: the message of salvation combined with pounding your opponent's face into the dirt.

The Heart of Texas museum was housed in the old jailhouse. There was an old man inside, who spent his days waiting in the gloom for visitors who rarely, if ever, arrived. I was the first living soul he had seen in three days. Why the museum was open on Good Friday I don't know. Perhaps he was the local atheist, a believer in exploding atoms and monkeys that transform themselves into men.

Anyway, I explored the converted jailhouse for a while, and it was a fascinating place, stuffed with weird detritus from the history of the town, such as old Swedish Bibles, photographs of beauty queens from the late 1950s and special jackets for turkeys, apparently to stop them from raping each other. The exhibits were all placed behind bars inside the old cells, some of which preserved ancient graffiti carved into the walls: 'HELP! I am being held captive!' cried one ghost; 'HELP ME!' shrieked another. The long dead Dwayne Brandon was more relaxed, content merely to record the date he had been imprisoned: 1899.

Perhaps Dwayne was wrong to be so at ease with his destiny, however. On the second floor I discovered the jail's noose, which was hanging above a trapdoor, with the lever nearby, just waiting to be pulled. A shop window dummy had been condemned to death and lay in the cell next to the noose, a mere metre or two away from the instrument of his future throttling, which he could see through the bars. Desperate to forget his coming execution, the dummy stared at the ceiling, a Bible lying open on his chest. I looked and saw that he had been reading the Old Testament book of Zechariah. It struck me as a curious choice – I would have thought most condemned men would opt for the gospels, with their message of personal resurrection and eternal life. And yet Zechariah is also uplifting as the prophet promises the Israelites that God will restore them to Jerusalem, where they will one day live safe from their enemies and cleansed of all sin.

Just down from the condemned dummy however I discovered something truly amazing, almost mystical. Hanging on the bars of a cell was a framed certificate from the Texas Board of Pharmacy dated 1888. I looked close and saw, written in the swirling calligraphy of the period, my name: *Kalder.* Well, not exactly my name – the certificate had been awarded to Mary Kalder, not Daniel. Even so, it felt like a message from the beyond, a sign that I was on the right path, that this journey did have a point, even if it wasn't yet clear to me. Was this a long lost relative? Were there other Kalders buried in Fife? And what had become of this Kalder, Mary? Where were her descendants? Did I have secret cousins lurking in the vicinity? Fife now felt a lot closer. In a strange and mysterious way it felt like I was returning home.

Downstairs the old man interrogated me about what I was doing in Texas. I told him that I had come to visit Fife, that I was from the original Fife, and that I wanted to see how our colony was faring. Had it taken root, had the original settlers made the right decision to leave Scotland, or should they have hung around in the mud and the rain with the rest of us?

He stared at me, calmly waiting for silence to force the foreigner to talk sense.

'Actually,' I said, slightly apologetically, 'I've heard there's nothing left.'

He continued staring. That didn't make sense either. Why go somewhere if you know there's nothing there? The silence dragged on.

'I'm on a road trip, just passing through. I heard about Fife, which is where I'm from in Scotland, and thought I'd have a look. I found my name upstairs by the way.'

The old man nodded. That last version explained my presence in Brady best. He could accept it, even though it wasn't true. He wasn't interested in the detail about the name though, not at all. He pulled out a map to show me Fife, which was a tiny point lurking just beyond a crossroads a few miles out of town. He reflected a minute and then spoke: 'You know, I think there might still be people living out there. Two or three years ago I was working at a local wholesalers, and I got a phone call from the general store in Fife. It was a strange, tired old voice, at the end of a crackly line. As I recall, they wanted ice.'

'Ice?'

'It gets mighty hot out there.'

I nodded. This was intriguing. Life? In Fife? I had assumed from the beginning that it was completely dead, that I would discover precisely nothing. This changed everything, not necessarily for the better. The old man continued nodding. Then he stopped:

'Actually the call was from the General Store in Doole, further out. No, there's nothing at all in Fife.'

And now, at last it was time to return to the land of my forefathers, who had set sail from America so long ago, crossing the Atlantic in order to colonise Scotland. As we all know the Comanche tribe landed their great ships on the freezing, wet shores of Fife on 2nd November 1698, establishing a colony there. The naive Fifers at first helped the strange visitors in the fantastical headdresses, giving them turnips to eat, linen to wear and thick black Bibles to read. However this was an error, because the tomahawks and exotic diseases of the Comanche soon cut a swathe through the indigenous people, reducing them to a wretched stump, living on the worst land in the region, i.e. Glenrothes where today their tragic descendants sniff glue, drink aftershave and occasionally rape street dogs. In the major towns of Dunfermline, Kirkcaldy and Saint Andrews the old churches and stone houses were pulled down to make way for the landscape of Fife as we know it today – littered as it is with totem poles, water proof teepees, and, of course, an abundance of pound shops.

Wait a minute – I got a little mixed up there. That last bit should be the other way round. It was Scots who settled the American Fife – an Alexander and Isabella Mitchell to be precise, who arrived with their children in 1878, eight years after Texas was readmitted to the union following the Civil War. They set up a little farm eighteen miles north of Brady. Other colonists soon joined them, and in 1882 the town received its name from a certain Mrs Finlay, who was nostalgic for her birthplace across the Atlantic Ocean. After that, well ... not a lot. In 1890 Fife got a school, which is nice – Henry H. Smith was the teacher. You remember Henry don't you? No? Actually, neither do I. In 1902 the growing population justified a post office, indicating that the town was expected to continue developing. By 1914 there were two general stores, a cotton gin and the population had hit 200. Then the rot set in. At the end of the 1940s only fifty people remained and the school had closed. People were departing for greener pastures, better towns, land that was less rocky, easier to farm. Or maybe they were just dying, and assuming their eternal positions beneath the ground. By the turn of the millennium, the population was down to 32. And now? Well....

The old man wasn't wrong. Fife was indeed in a state of advanced ghostliness. Most of it had been swallowed by a ranch which had stolen the town's name. Where houses had stood there were now vast flat fields, surrounded by an electric fence and numerous warnings to trespassers to keep out. Crops, insects, animals, were ruthlessly devouring the memory of the life that had been. Soon Fife would disappear entirely, like the Indian tribes who had roamed these plains before the white men arrived, except with one major difference: people are still interested in the Indians. Before it reached that point however the current interim period – when a few fragments of the past lingered suggestively – would continue a little longer. These fragments were chronically inconclusive however – blank like skulls, with the identifying skin and meat and hair removed. They persist mainly to frustrate us, to hint at lost mysteries that cannot be retrieved.

Aside from the ranch this is what remained:

A road, stretching into the distance.

A pile of old wood, the ruins of somebody's home, surrounded by enormous cacti that were growing in the spaces where the old rooms had been. Dry and brittle, the wood was ready to disintegrate in flames.

Across the road from the wood there was a caravan, which probably housed migrant workers employed by the ranch that had eaten Fife. Nobody was home. Perhaps they were out working in the fields, burning to death in the apocalyptic heat as they earned a few dollars to send home to their families in Mexico. They did not belong here in this landscape; they would escape as soon as their work was done.

Just beyond the caravan there was a windmill. But there was no wind.

Next door to the windmill stood the remains of the old schoolhouse, a wooden shell in the process of being pulled down to the earth by trees and bushes. I walked towards it, to stare in the windows and commune with the spirit of education. Could I detect the ghostly presence of boys and girls, absorbing knowledge decades earlier? No. After it had been abandoned by children in the 1940s, the school had been converted into a barn and served as a shelter for hogs from the heat. But now the hogs were all gone, too.

In the long grass meanwhile lay assorted pieces of rubbish: beer cans, tossed from the windows of passing cars. Some animal bones. A human tooth. The most significant artifact was a baseball, lying not far from school. It was faded and ancient, and had been there for some time, perhaps a relic of the last game of baseball played in the town before it died. I pocketed it, as a memento, so that the memory of Fife would not fade from the earth entirely.

Finally I located some goats, chewing grass in the yard of a house that appeared to be inhabited – possibly by the last human in Fife. He didn't want to talk however – an enormous dog strained at its leash by a gate that was locked shut. When I approached, the hound exploded in murderous rage. It was ready to fight hordes of zombies, risen from the grave, armies of invading commies, Nazis, Comanche raiding parties, anyone. Just leave the house alone.

After about thirty minutes I retraced my steps to make sure there was nothing I had missed, and then paused one last time to take in the prospect of all our fates, which of course is one of the things that Fife represents. It had been a good journey, very instructive, filled with resonance, even if I wasn't sure exactly what it was that was resonating.

And yet, in a sense I hadn't been to Fife at all because Fife cannot be visited. You see, the signs marking the entrance and exit to the town are fastened to the same pole. The city limits are thus separated by two inches of space. Technically, then, Fife is not a town at all, not even a ghost town. It is a slice of sky sandwiched between two metal plates. Everything else I had seen – the wood, the windmill, the abandoned school – were somehow outside, beyond Fife, in a literal no man's land.

Fife itself had been reduced to nothingness, or as close as is possible on this earth. I will admit I had a strange desire to transform myself into air, and float up there to nestle in the space between the signs, warmed by the rays of a distant sun. But I know that it is good that I could not, because I think I might never have left.

The moon in a cave untying its travelling bundle

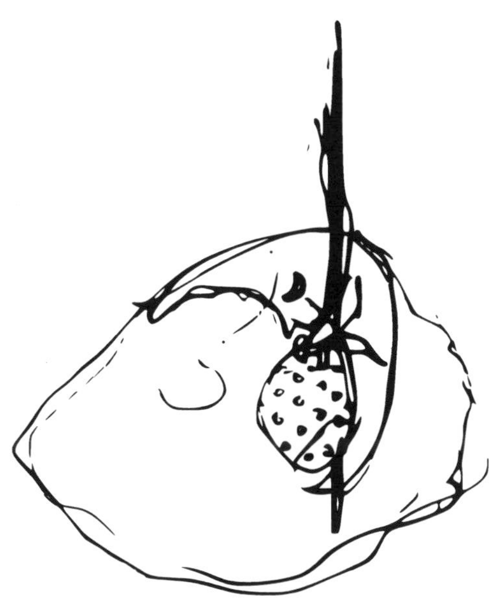

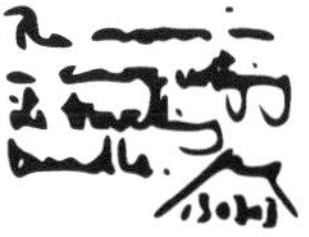

ROBERT STARK

QUEEN OF THE HAUGH

Queen of the Haugh
Suspended in a clearing
That afternoon,
Was it evening?
That summer when the heat was all
Across Kincardine town,
The Firth of Forth
Still down to the railroad bridge,
Arthur's seat;
& in the shadows that we count
Along the valley ridge
A clarity that cuts & keeps.

There's still that evening eight years on:
Your voice was time itself.
We lay
Stations
On the Bel rock shelf
& passed the longest day,
I saw the Pict in you & me,
The governance of love's slow, leeward sense
From the valley ridge to the silvered sea.
Now winter is the conscience lies between us
Nothing but the past upon us
All the clocks turned back.

CICADAS & LISA

Now the red leaves show
O Lisa, where are you?
Now the sun is low
Lisa, & the day is through?

For the birds they are squabbling
Lisa, settling in the trees,
& lovers are assembling
As night comes on by slow degrees.

The cicadas sing out
O Lisa, in their manner;
As Plato says, their song's about
All the gods we honour.

But where are you, Lisa,
Now the birds are silent,
Now that the heat is lesser
& the lovers all have went;

Now no leaf shows, Lisa,
& there is no sun,
& I am like the cicada
Crying for oblivion?

THE AUSPICA ARE DUMB

The auspica are dumb,
Give cry: the palsy comes
Like never of yore
The hailest go in fear

Like unto Cassandra
Discovered in the skein;
Loxias' regalia
Squaring up to the squad:

Many dark words of god.

The prone canticle
Of sapience is cut
Down to the cuticle,
The hot seam of the quick:

Dark words
& the blood comes thick.

A WOMAN IS DROWNING

A woman is drowning
Below the surface she is stuck
Sinking rapidly, continuously.
Medusa-like her tangled hair
Is eddying, obscuring &
Exposing a face: features wash
Across the dreamer's gaze.

The reflection of the sky,
The susurrations of the waves imply
She is not one but two, perhaps
She is every woman & maybe
She has no face at all.

Her vague, tragical moment
Seems articulated to
The unremembered past;
A deliberate, necessary placing
Between life & death:
The terror is exquisite.

What rescue does the dream propose?
What line is cast? What failed attempt
As the dream dissolves?

Trembling on waking I know
The saving line was you
& that sunken body
It was mine.

THE WATER MUST HAVE RISEN IMPERCEPTIBLY

The water must have
Risen imperceptibly,
Amplitudes of morse
Disguising it & then
Silence, & below
That sure freeze.

Four forgetful days
Of slow discovery.
This creviced mass
Tumesces, more
Water is displaced
Something dislodges
All our bulk in the end.

A slight animation
Startles the fish,
Buoyancy: slow
Awful ascension.
A tiny thawing
& then more slowly

Rapping through
The slender icefolds
Among the rubbish
In the light of day,
The first nice day
For a walk by the river:
A body.

I HAVE STARED UPON THE SNOW

I have stared upon the snow
So long it has turned black,
        For all bright things know
        The surest woe
Despite what shallow senses track.

& as the moon looms toward eclipse
Which formerly was winter white
        So sweet love's lip
        Trembling, trips
& leers, insensible in loveless spite;

For this is the world riven mad,
& now is the angered god
        spuming forth,
Blighting all creation's birth;

Now are garbled messages,
        Now direst presages;
No significance or worth
Is writ on the profane earth;

I have looked upon the snow
        Too long I fear,
For now are senses slow
& senseless death draws near.

ON BATTLING TIDES

From where Lake Michigan throws
Thrashing its hills & hollows
To where the force is choked
Irresistibly
On this beach-bed of rock
One warning comes:
                                        that strength is spent
Though we only play
Though we delve & vent
We are cut & smoothed the same,
Unceremoniously
Cast in sand & loam;
                                        bright gems
Once, perhaps, & lustrous,
That had made love known.

EXTRICATE

The assumption that love leads us
Toward happiness is false
It leads nowhere
Love is a road to leave off

In all we have striven most
Vainly to communicate in love
To be well understood we have
Only lost

                    for life will have its jokes
& its symbolism. My life is this
Trying to withstand the force
Of simplicity & chaos –

How much has love to do with these

How it forebears to be understood

WE HAVE THE LAKESIDE PARK ALL TO OURSELVES

We have the lakeside park all to ourselves,
April is cold & beautiful & light,
The buoyant laughter of the wind-borne gulls
Circling & rioting incites
A feeling that we had supposed subdued,
But now we walk together once again
& remember that lightsomeness of mood
That comes around, it doubtlessly remains.
I recognize this feeling, know today
Will be filled in dreamy going-about,
Pretenses & fitful activity
To greet the world while hushed & devout
I bid you summon me & keep me by
Your side though all of errant space denies.

SEASCAPE

Diana
Of night & love

Is here: her dark
Her silver

The irrelevant universe
Ever at her back

Making & unmaking
In slow uncreation

Her chaos
All intending form.

An art of perception
Her motioning,

Dedicated, carnal,
The utter knowing

Of the sea,
The Earth's longing

For her womb.

DIRGE

Time has orphaned us, Sister
We hedge apart
& never really can catch up

Alas, for death has one
By one done in
These figments, life:

The stunned solitude
Of the old alone is left
Beautiful & black

Beyond the skyline
Calomel aglow, clouds
Mock the stillness in our hearts:

Brooding dark, glistening,

The thunder starts.

The big frog

The big fog.

IAIN BAHLAJ

CAUGHT SHORT IN MID CALDER

PRESENTED as a simple equation it might go something like this:

> *C (urry) + H (eat) + J (ob interview nerves) + T (raffic) + P (oor service station facilities) = H (im going feral for 16 hours)*

Real life never ran like that, however, it didn't have the same flow, from start to finish. Each individual factor never did its job and then politely fucked off; they ganged up, tag-teamed him, or enacted something resembling the CCTV footage of some poor bastard being filled in by a gang that you might catch on one of the digital channels you find yourself watching, the channels whose names you never bother to learn.

He'd had the curry two nights previous. Most people would assume that the cause of any food-poisoning or, posh-speak, an 'iffy tummy', must be something from the previous day, but he knew it didn't because The Day Job had sent him on a course where he had learned, among other valuable things, that in actual fact food poisoning takes a few days to develop.

It was a Madras curry. It arrived with a miserable looking guy playing Happy Hardcore from his run-down Renault Megan. When they locked eyes there was a feeling of solidarity, or at least our hero sensed it. The both of them, stuck in these shitty jobs. Both in the food business, both serving up raw materials for clogging arteries and inducing health problems in later life. He doubted that the delivery guy had pursued higher education like you were supposed to, but still, he couldn't imagine delivering takeaways being an adequate lifetime ambition. When he asked the amount the guy said 'six pound twenty man' and he said 'there's seven, keep the change' and winked at him. When he closed the door he worried it might be taken as some kind of gay come-on rather than workers' solidarity.

He bought Madras because, through trial and error, he realised it was the curry they put the least amount of onions in. This saved him time in picking them out. He could ask on the phone for a curry to be made with no onions but he didn't like to; he imagined the cook being hard-done by, as disenfranchised as he was, with any type of anally retentive request likely to set him off and have him opening his wrists onto a large nan.

It tasted fine, but it always does. Food-poisoning, it's all microbiological, beyond the taste-buds of the common man.

That morning, in the flat, the food-poisoning lay dormant. He woke after a nervous, jittery, three-hours maximum sleep to the sun splitting the blinds. After completing his thirty-minute morning washing ritual, he dressed into The New Suit, which he had purchased for approximately two week's wages because it was a kind-of metallic grey, and was the closest thing he could find that resembled a suit he'd watched a football player wear as he attempted to analyse some football match (though that would undoubtedly have been designer, maybe Hugo Boss, or Helmut Lang). The New Suit seemed to say success, youth, energy, and ambition: all of the buzzwords he would mention at the interview, to deflect attention away from the prickly issue of 'experience'. In the game of interview bullshit trumps he hoped that a combination of those four words, in spoken-word and clothing form, might win.

As he locked the flat he noticed his hands were shaking. He chuckled to himself like a madman. It wasn't a big deal; but it was.

While not 'the dream job' it was the closest thing he could imagine in the waking world. Since leaving University he'd been forced to quit reaching for the sky/dreaming of the penthouse suite. Instead he would happily settle for the basement, in a suitable building.

But the thought of doing a job he'd actually set out, all these years ago, to do, seemed like a fairytale ending in what politicians might refer to as 'the current climate'. To go into work and not feel like crying, an end to stopping working for a second and wondering if this is it, your life; no more fantasies about massacring employees and customers and burning the place to the ground.

His hands still shook as he opened the door to his small two-door car. The sun shone like a spotlight, a bead of sweat appeared on his brow. His reflection stared back uneasily from the driver's side window; he thought it looked like a man waiting to walk the plank.

Inside the car the air seemed thick, muggy, heavy in his lungs. He took a deep breath, let a head rush fizzle out, and started the engine.

It was one of those mystery traffic jams, with no obvious cause. As soon as he trundled upon it he switched *The Best Of Roxy Music* off, cutting the supposed-to-help-relaxation 'Avalon' out mid-sentence, and tuned to local radio. No mention of cause, only the effect, no mention of the disease, only the symptoms.

Last year he had been driving back from work and the bridge had been closed, but by the time, past the point of no return/last sliproad, he had no other option but to wait, as the police cars crept back and forward. It took two hours; he missed both *The Apprentice* and its offshoot, *The Apprentice:You're Fired.* He heard later from someone that knew someone that some guy had climbed the tower, drunk, and was going to jump; but he hadn't. He'd missed *both* programmes, he remembered – briefly, before guilt put a stop – thinking, and the guy *hadn't even jumped.*

What if this job went tits-up? How many other applicants would there be? How would they be dressed âĂŞ maybe they'd be some hot-shot from an uppercrust family with a *real* Helmut Lang suit.

The heat in the car seemed to rise; sweat dripping down the side of his face felt like blood. His shirt-sleeves started moistening, pressing against his flesh; his stomach spasmed, his intestines seemed to contract; his internal organs he imagined going off in the heat; no longer fit for purpose, have to be wasted....

The traffic nudged forward; he sat with one leg deadweight on the clutch, the other switched between brake and accelerator.

And there was every chance it would go tits up, in today's climate, there was probably a production line of exceptional candidates.

It could be years before another job arrived, another opportunity.

Nudging forward another inch.

Years of this shit, of scraping a living, coming home to the empty flat, the same drudgery. How did previous generations do it? The pits, the factories. They took it for granted that work would be monotonous, they handled it. Went home to their wives, a drink on a Friday, Saturday, Sunday.

But he worked those nights.

Ten years later everything might still be the same.

Time was passing him by.

He could feel it, its hot air against his face, swimming over him like one of those graphics used to demonstrate aerodynamics.

The traffic lurched forward.

This Was It. The Most Important Morning Of His Life.

He was needing the toilet NOW, could feel it happening. Now as in NOW, not in two minutes, not maybe ten minutes. He needed a toilet NOW, the traffic to part like the Red Sea.

He blew this, ten years later, same job, same misery.

Hallelujah, the traffic started to shift.

His petrol light bleeped.

A sign said 'services 2 miles'.

He took a deep breath, held it in, and pushed the accelerator.

Everyone has 'accidents'. Last time he was six, at his Gran's, at some social event. Everyone drinking, laughing. But she never had a bathroom door, more of a shutter, some kind of jaggy plastic contraption he'd never seen since. It had a lock, a tiny, slide-over thing; but this day the lock was broken. All that stood between him and a drunken member of his extended family was that thing, lightweight, plastic … shutter-thing.

So he held it in. Hours. Holding it in. Everyone eating, laughing. He sat in the corner, his stomach clenched, sweating.

And, six hours later, he almost made it. Almost. To the end of the drive.

Years later, a different scene: Spain, a bus holiday. He watched an old man, almost definitely senile, as he wandered around with a brown stinking stain on the back of his beige chinos, and running down to his white socks. He was twelve, or thereabouts, but already knew the proper adult behaviour in this situation. He ignored it, acted like nothing had happened.

Only one woman acknowledged the horror of what had happened. She asked the man for the cardigan he was wearing. Confused, he gave her it, and she tied it around his waist.

It was one of those all-in-one things. A rival fast food outlet, with some kind of coffee house, and a petrol station. He drove up like something out of an American 70s cop show; to complete the illusion he might have slid, on one arse-cheek, across the bonnet of the car.

He managed a: where's the toilets? to the girl behind the little sweet shop counter. The sweat trickled down his temples, through sideburns; his shirt stuck to his flesh in patches; she said over there. He followed, went inside.

The urinals lay on the right, four cubicles on the left. Two men stood at either end of the block of urinals, pissing happily as they considered their own reflections.

One turned as he approached.

He found himself nodding.

His hair felt wet.

His bowels clenched, struggling to hold out. He imagined steel girders creaking in the strain of the sun.

Inside the first cubicle he reached for the door and the....

There wasn't a lock.

What was a trickle of sweat became a flood.

His stomach groaned.

What options?

He sat there, waited it out, sat on the toilet seat, fully clothed, arched forward, clenching.

After two minutes of handwashing and blowdrying, silence fell upon the toilets.

He ventured out.

To the second cubicle, with no lock.

God god god.

Shaking, his whole body just dipped in sweat, like his pores were salivating over the thought....

The third cubicle, no lock.

No no

The fourth....

No no no no

Jesus Christ, he thought to himself. What kind of state of affairs was this? A modern country, Britain, the largest Empire in the history of man-fucking-kind and it was beyond our reach to provide our public bogs with locks, or replace them whenever some shameless vandal knocked them off?

He considered it, for a moment, sitting there, with one hand, or a foot maybe, on the door. Until someone else entered, and that made up his mind.

He scurried outside.

America … as civilised as Britain maybe, but in America the toilets always seemed to have those mid-length doors, like the fucking saloon doors in a John Wayne film … and no locks … but that was the Yanks, whatever happened to British Victorian repression?

He considered asking the girl, Disabled Toilets? But no, he couldn't, why would she oblige, he was obviously physically fit, and stable. He hadn't seen any on the way in, there was no time to look.

Outside, the sun spotlighting him again, he felt small, insignificant. A tiny speck of matter.

Another rival fast foot chain lay across the car park. He made his way with purpose, keys already in his hand, bowels ready to burst; until he dropped them (the keys) and bend down in too-quick a motion and:

Fuck.

The wetness started off a tiny patch, then spread, slinking down the inside of his thighs, soaking the back of his trousers and, infant-style, his lower back and the bottom of his shirt.

A quick look round. No witnesses. Well, one, but he was in front, twenty feet away, but approaching.

No other thing for it, he ran, 70s cop style – it seemed to be recurring motif) – to his car, conscious of the stain that would be getting bigger, on the Helmut Lang rip-off suit.

The man probably eyed him with suspicion, or bemusement.

He didn't look to see.

More than anything in the world he needed the enclosed space, the sweet seclusion, of that molten chunk of metal.

Inside he reversed, spun, accelerated.

Maybe it was possible to go home, change clothes, come back? Maybe all was not lost.

His car welcomed back. It said: You can rely on me to keep your secret. But those words sounded like an alarm, a bleeping noise.

Food poisoning. He would wonder, later, after he recovered and was relatively back to normal, if maybe it had some effects on the brain, if maybe, like other viruses, it had grown more sophisticated with time.

He was eight miles from the bridge, the smell was thick in the air, provoking images of Dickensian London and open sewers and typhoid and other diseases he'd wikipedia'd bored a few weeks previous. He didn't dare open the windows in case a passing motorist caught a whiff and cast an accusing glare in his direction.

There was no way he was going to make it.

He knew that.

At this point, in a dream, he would ponder the ridiculousness of the situation: trapped in a car on a boiling hot day, running out of petrol, having shat yourself in your best suit. Usually, that self-awareness would cause him to wake up with a jolt.

Not today thought.

It required better thinking.

He thought back to the old man. Why did he seem so un-bothered? Walking around in shit-stained chinos, anyone else would die, but he seemed as contented and chuffed as anyone. Why?

Because he was almost definitely senile.

He was not *conscious* of it.

The potential mortifying embarrassment could only hurt him if he was conscious.

If he was to be unconscious, oblivious, blissfully ignorant, it would be fine.

And the woman, with the old man, said 'I'm a nurse' to someone. He distinctly remembered.

Nurses, doctors, ambulance men. They're the one group of people an adult is allowed to embarrass themselves in front of. They probe every nook and cranny, clinically, professionally, forgetting it is a person; it was simple.

The pieces fell into place in his fevered brain.

All he had to do was crash the car. Not badly enough to cause death, but bad enough to cause a loss of consciousness.

The ambulance drivers would spirit him to a nice clean sterile air-conditioned hospital.

The nurses would treat him like a life-size doll and dress him up all nice in hospital gowns for the tea-party they were going to have him have with doctors . . .

And there you have it.

Forty should do it, he thought, and he slowed down until near forty, aimed for a tree past the ditch on the left, and swerved.

The Golf bounced happily off the dual carriageway, bounced again, bumper first, into the ditch, veered to the right and hit a smaller, less stable tree than He had hoped for, causing the tree to snap, the airbag to burst out of the steering wheel like an attention-seeking whoopee cushion. And, once he had bounced face first onto it, and then back onto the headrest, then forward again; towards the end of that second face to-airbag-contact, he vomited; over the airbag, his chin, tie, shirt. . . .

Throughout it all, consciousness, though jolted, manhandled, strangled, stayed the course.

It was thirty minutes later, he was tired from running. He had definitely lost them, the concerned motorists, coming to check if he was okay. He had been smart enough to run in the general direction of the bridge.

It was simple. He would follow the road, but not too close. Scurrying over farmer's fields, using trees as cover, staying under the radar. He would be hungry later, but that posed no problem. He could steal a turnip, smash it on a fencepost, feast on the clean flesh inside.

According to the Google map he'd accessed on his iPhone he was approximately twelve miles from the bridge. He would have to find a hideout, kill time, until night fell. Under cover of darkness he would cross the bridge, and then, only fourteen miles until home. If he needed encouragement he might climb a pylon, get a view of home, to boost morale.

He was amazed at his own resourcefulness; at the way he could clearly identify his goals, set his targets, and forumulate a plan to achieve them. If his potential employers only knew ... if only they could see him now. He had it all, the youth, the success, the energy, ambition.

He would make it.

In a moment of inspiration, the icing-on-the-cake if you will, he removed his vomit-stained tie, looked at it, and then tied it, Rambo-style, around his head, and set off....

Sleep with one eye open, old man

ROSS WILSON

THE ABBEY WALK

I walked through Dunfermline Abbey a year ago
on a Sunday morning in summer alone, watching
motes rise in light fall in shadow between walls
where many passed before me. Silence ended in

the few minutes my shoes tapped over old stones.
I stepped through an arch into the sun and saw
ruins of a palace built by men
who lived and prayed, loved and died.

KING ROBERT THE BRUCE crowned ground
his heartless body was interred centuries before –
The Black Douglas went on his way to some
Middle Eastern war with that kings heart

and threw it away in Spain with his life.
In shadows of old stones I saw a memorial for
those who went on their way to new wars
swift as swallows sheltered briefly as I was

a year ago already, walking through Dunfermline
Abbey alone – five hundred years after Henryson
walked in certainty of a light out as those flown
century through century, quickly so quickly. Only

their names and dates cut into stones.
And their birdsongs caught in poems.

Robert Henryson was a medieval poet and schoolmaster attached to Dunfermline Abbey. He wrote a poem called The Abbey Walk.

THE WAY JOHN WENT OUT

In memory of John Gray

I had you in my corner a few years,
talking me into, and through pain.

Weekends, you'd take me into
Edinburgh and Glasgow to train;
mid-week, we worked out in Rosyth.
Days in-between, I ran alone.

We were about the same height then:
Five three, flyweights. I, fourteen, all bone, you, a trim
        forty,
fitter than anyone in the gym, until I caught up, like time

caught us six years later.
A six foot welterweight that day
we met, books tucked under what had been a left hook,
        specs on a never
broken nose.

I was awoken that day
like a brawler too clumsy to duck
the surprise counter of your news.
The best punches come from nowhere.

This one hit before we could begin.
A doctor stepped between us, waving it all off; a time-
        keeper beat the
slow count out of days before a bell could ring.

And it was a daze to stumble into,
like those nights when I'd run alone
in the dark of a wood, no stool to rest on, and no voice
    in the corner
where I once stood

tired and bloodied with your hand
flying my hand like the kite
we were both high as, walking
down the steps of Meadowbank Stadium,

1993. You came in with nothing, you
said to me, you went out a champion.

The Way John Went Out *was originally published in* AGENDA (Broadsheet 8) *in 2007.*

TIMESHARE

NOTE: *The following excerpt is from chapter three of a novel* TIMESHARE.

It's been over two hundred years since a volcano erupted on Lanzarote. But when three generations of the same family holiday together in a small apartment the earth is set to split open again.

Calum has quit his job and English home to care for his dad Wullie, a retired miner recovering from a stroke, and takes him to Lanzarote with his estranged son Scott, a twenty five year old waster.

SCOTT was watching the telly with his feet stretched out on the glass table and a bottle of San Miguel balanced precariously on his knee when Calum slid the glass doors open and Wullie stumbled in.

— Ye huv a guid meal di? Scott shouted.

— *Huh-hi!* Wullie said, disappearing into his bedroom.

— Did you go out with the lassie? Calum asked Scott.

— Aye.

:Calum looked at him. — She's workin in the bar. I just seen her.

Scott stared back. — Well, thir must be two lassies in Lanzarote then, eh? Yir blockin the telly.

Calum moved.

— She couldnae git the night aff, Scott mumbled.

— So you just sat here?

— Aye.

Calum looked at the sand on the soles of Scott's sandals, and at the DIY tattoo on his forearm. It was supposed to be a saltire, but Calum had always thought it looked like a cross a teacher might score in a jotter to let you know you'd got something wrong. He was about to say something, when Scott got in first.

— Ma di enjoy ihs sel?

— Aye.

Scott sipped his lager, flicking the label on the bottle, as Wullie shuffled into the living room in a cardigan and flip flops.

— You need your nebuliser dad? Calum asked.

— Ih?

— *Yir neb?*

— Ah'm fine, Wullie insisted, pressing the button on the microwave. The door opened and he put his straw hat inside, clicked the door shut, and shuffled to the couch, chucking his bum bag on the bunker. Euros spilled across the floor.

— Funny folk, the Chinks, Wullie said.

— You shouldn't call them that dad, Calum told him, retrieving the scattered coins.

— Hoo no? Wullie frowned, turning at the couch, - that's what the ir.

— They're *Chinese,* Calum corrected him, sitting on the far end of the couch from Scott.

— Aye, n you're Scottish n you're a *Scot.* Chinese: Chink. Pakistani: Paki. It's aw the same thing.

Scott laughed as Wullie half sat, paused, and free fell into the space between Calum and Scott, elbowing Scott's beer bottle into his teeth.

— *Christ sake di!*

He wiped at the spillage down his shirt and dabbed his lips and gums, checking for blood, then smiled, nudging Wullie. — Here, di! he said, — how dae Chinkie's name thir bairns?

— Nae idea.

— The throw somethin oan the floor n listen fir the noise it makes: *ping pong ting ching a-ling!*

Wullie laughed as Calum shook his head and Scott elbowed his di again.

— Thir's a Chinky oan ma computer course di. Guess what wi call uh'm?

— Nae idea.

— *Ping Pong!*

Wullie chuckled, and Calum nearly mentioned how they might call Scott Ned Kelly, but didn't bother, figuring the reference to the hard headed outlaw and neds would be lost on him, and anyway, it wasn't worth the trouble.

— Ye wantin a beer di? Scott asked.

— Aye.

Calum looked at Scott. — He'll need his medication soon Scott.

Scott tutted. — A beer'll no hurt.

— He's had too many G n' T's this afternoon is it is.

Scott shook his head, but Wullie said, — Aye, yir faither's right son.

— You want wan? Scott asked Calum.

— No.

Scott ripped the tab from another bottle with his teeth and spat it in the sink.

Calum stared at him.

Scott stared back. — *What?*

Calum looked at the telly as Scott walked back to the couch.

— Turn it up, Wullie said, nodding at the telly.

Scott reached for the remote and turned the volume up.

Half a dozen men and a woman sat behind a half moon table before an audience.

— That looks like *Question Time,* Wullie said.

— It is.

— *Here?*

— Ye get all the British channels here dad.

Wullie's eyebrows fluttered. — Dae ye? Did you ken that Scott?

— Aye, Ah'v been here before.

— What's the questions son?

— Iraq, Calum said, looking at the paper in his lap.

Scott folded his arms and rested his feet on the table, looking through its glass surface to his glossy lads' mag on the floor and the airbrushed image of flesh it framed. Calum turned the page of his Scotsman, and Wullie hunched towards the telly, head at an angle favouring his hearing aid.

A fly swooped from the light, buzzing between their heads, as the TV presenter stated the recent figures despatched to Iraq.

— *Here!* Scott son, Wullie said, nudging Scott's knee, — no bae long noo afore the conscript you, ih?

— Aye, *right,* Scott snorted, backhanding the fly irritably.

— The Black Watch, ih Scott son?

— Ah'd rethir eat mae ayn flesh di.

Wullie laughed, turning his attention back to the programme where a woman said something about the collapse of infrastructure, chaos, disorder....

— Thiv jist made awthin worse ye know, Wullie said.

— Here we go, Calum sighed.

— So the huv, Wullie insisted, — like the lassie there's sayin, oan the telly there, thiv jist made it worse, fir terrorists like.

— They had to go in dad.

— Pish.

— Ye can't let folk like Saddam run amok.

— *It's aw tae dae wi oil!*

Calum sighed. — Things are more complicated than that dad.

— Things id be simple anuff if people didnae complicate thum! Thiv nae right tae be there! It's aw money, that's aw it is, that's the only reason the gan oanywhere n the world! Tae exploit the poor! *Thir jist wantin tae take er the world!*

Calum laughed.

— *Ach!* Wullie glowered with frustration as Scott's head lolled back on the couch and his eyes rolled back in their sockets.

— Christ, they've no life as it is dad, Calum said, — this'll give them a chance at democracy.

— *It'll be the ruin ih the place!*

— It's a shithole oanywiy, Scott mumbled, sitting up to reach for his lager.

— Maybe, Calum reasoned with his dad, ignoring Scott, — but least they'll be free of Saddam's regime.

— Imperialism's aw it is!

Calum laughed.

— Aye, yir laughin!

— Look dad, do you think ... do you seriously think folk in the Third World get as heated about it is you do?

— *Thir blawin thir sells up aboot it!*

— That's pretty heated up, Scott sniggered.

— All I'm trying to say is things are complex.

— It's folk like you thit fuckin complicates things! You jist give in you!

— No, dad, you give in. You give in to anger ...

— So wid you be fuckin angry!

— But look, would you listen a minute. Anger, resentment, where do they get anybody?

— You forget where Ah come fae sir! Yeh'v turned against yir ayn people.

A smile sealed Calum's lips.

— Aye, yir smilin.

— Look, dad ...

— *Ach!*

— How do we know Iraq hasn't nuclear capabilities or isn't a haven for terrorists? We don't. That's why we've got to ...

— *It's the oil Ah'm tellin ye!*

Calum groaned. — It's got nothing to do with oil dad.

And Scott sighed as he stood up. — Oh yes it is, oh no it isn't! How kin either ih yehs know what it's aw aboot? Ah mean, yehs sit there so convinced yir right, bit how will ye ivir know? We dinnae huv the information they boays huv access tae.

Scott waved his hand at the politician talking.

— The jist tell us what the want, he said, — then dress up what the do know tae manipulate folk so's thi'll take their side.

Wullie looked at his grandson. — Aye, he said, — bit ye cannae jist no huv opinions son.

— That's a matter ih opinion di.

Wullie pointed his finger at the telly. — *This is serious business in the world, this!*

— It's none ih ma business.

— *Bit it is son! It's awbdys fuckin business!*

Laughter doubled Scott up like a punch in the stomach as saliva frothed Wullie's lips and veins turned up the heat in his head.

— You're wastin your breath dad, Calum snorted, — he doesn't believe in anything, him.

— Hoo dae ye git that like? Scott snapped.

— I'm not arguing with you Scott.

— Aye, cause yeh'v no an argument, that's wiy!

— Wheeshed! Wullie demanded, — Ah cannae hear the telly!

The fly buzzed between their heads, avoiding Calum's swatting palm, to rest on the image of a politician, until the image changed and scared it away.

— The dinnae even ken what thir bloody aimin it! Wullie snapped, aiming the remote at the telly. He shot the screen. The politician turned into a man, or a woman, Wullie wasn't sure what the fuck it was, explaining how men were beginning to realise just how important a taut stomach and cheekbones were in the difference between success and failure. 'Men are increasingly turning to plastic surgery' the presenter said, 'for business reasons as much as personal vanity.'

— The world's aff it's nut! Wullie cried, switching back to the politician.

Scott nudged him. — Mind you used tae tell mae Ah should uh'v joined the army tae learn a trade n fir self discipline n that di?

— Aye, in peace times son. Ah widnae want ye awo er there noo.

Calum looked up from his paper to his dad.

— Did you no try n walk to the war dad?

Scott sat up.

— Ah did, aye, Wullie said.

Scott was incredulous. — Ye tried tae walk tae the war?

— Wi wantit awo, Wullie said.

Scott snorted. — Tae git killed!

— It wis diffrint times son.

— A bullet's a bullet regardless ih the times di.

Calum looked at his son. — Folk where what you call 'patriotic' back then son, they thought differently. Duty meant someth …

— Pish, Wullie cut in, and Scott laughed as his di continued, — wi jist wantit awo. Ah mean, we nivir goat hoalidays tae Lanzarote then ye know. Wi wantit an adventure.

— So ye tried tae walk tae World War Two! What happened?

— Well, the widnae huv us, cause wi wir miners.

— So?

— So, the needed us tae stiy back hame, ken, tae work.

— Guid joab! Scott said, — me n ma dad might no be sittin here noo.

Footage of burnt out trucks and cars, caught from the unsteady perspective of a hand held camera, beamed into the living room.

— The widnae lit ye oot the pit, see, Wullie went on, — that's what the cried the 'Essential Work Order'. Ye couldnae leave the pit.

— Bit ye tried tae walk tae the war?

— Oh aye, me n Jimmy tried tae git awo tae the merchant navy twa or three times, Wullie said, his voice wheezy. — Bit, Christ, eftir what wi seen. Ah mean, the wir sinkin boats left right n centre. Bit, wi used tae gan doon tae Burnt Island. It hud the docks it that time, see. Thir wir merchant boats left there n ye could register there, bit, whenever ye said ye wir fae Fife, like, Ah mean, ye nivir *hud* tae say, ye ken, fir ye hud tae show an identity card n the *kent!*

'Git awo! You work doon the pit!'

Ach! So, then wi went tae Perth tae try tae jiyn the Black Watch. The widnae take ye. So, wi went tae Edinburgh. Ach, they widnae take ye. N wi wir wantin awo! Ye ken? The widnae take ye. Ye wir wantin oot the pit, see. So there ye are.

— Did Jimmy not try and walk over the Forth Railway bridge dad? I think I remember you sayin that one time.

Scott shook his head and laughed as Wullie sat up a little. — Well, that's anithir story. Wi thought wid huv mair chance if wi goat tae Liverpool.

— *Liverpool!* Scott laughed, sitting up. He was on the edge of his seat.

— Well that's where the signed ye oan see.

— So what happened?

— Well, it wis Saturday nicht see. Wi wir in the Club, n Ah says tae Jimmy, Ah says 'ach, will walk doon.' Thir wisnae a loat ih transport it that time, thir wir nae cars or oanythin, wan or twa trains, bit they wir ey stowed wi sodgers.

So, wi set off, n wi . . . wi goat tae the Forth, through the nicht like, n Ah says 'will no git across here.' Ah says, 'Christ, wi kin walk er the brig' n that's you near anuff in Edinburgh, ken. So wi gits up tae the railway n thir wir a loat ih, no say much passengers, bit a loat ih goods trains, ken. So, Ah says, will wait till a train comes n will run along beside it tae git passed this wee box oan the brig. Thir wis a licht in it, see, wi a boay in there. So, Ah says tae Jimmy, will pit ir troosirs inside ir socks, fir wi wore wide troosirs it that time see. In case ye fell, ken. But! It wis *white* socks wi hud oan, eh, n *here!* The boay seen ir socks runnin alongside the train n ih came runnin oot hollerin *'ey! Come fuckin back!'* N Ah says 'that's aw wi need' n the boay goes 'where the fuck ir you boays gaun?' 'er the brig' ' ir yehs aff yir nut? Well, it's a guid joab Ah stoapped ye then.'

Ye see, the Sooth Queensferry side wis loaded wi sodgers, gaurdin the brig like. Ih says 'Christ, yir some boays.' So wi sat aside uh'm in the wee box, it's still there yit, and, eh … 'thir's a train it six o'clock in the mornin' ih telt us.

— Back hame? Scott asked.

— Naw, naw, tae gan er the brig.

Scott laughed.

— *So!* Wi hud tae buy a ticket tae gan er the brig. N that's what wi done. Oanywi! So wi set aff, n wi git tae … Ah says, 'now, thir's a tram car oan the other side, n that'll take us intae Edinburgh.' Cause ye wir cheaper wi trams see. Ah says it'll save us the legs a bit, cause wi hud a loat ih miles ahead ih us see. It went right doon Princes street, right doon bae the terminus, right sooth, like, tae the last stop. N that saved us a bit. N then wi started walkin. N wi goat, oh, way doon bae where? Galashiels Ah think. N then this polisman came along oan a wee motorbike. The wir ey lookin fir prisoners ih war, see. Bit the hud nae place tae go, Germans, cause thid need boats tae git oot ih Britain. Ah mean, it wis diffrint fir oor boays, they'd go tae Switzerland n places like that. Bit oanywi! The wir ey lookin fir deserters, n this boay goes

'where ir you'se gaun?'

'Liverpool'

'identity cards'

ach!

'Fife! Yehs miners? Better gan back now' ih says, 'thir's nae point gaun any further that wiy cause thi'll jist … thirs mair like me, see, n thi'll make ye go back, thi'll lift ye.' Arch, eftir walkin aw the wiy tae Galashiels. Knackered wi wir! Come back the nixt nicht, walkin aw the time.

— Did ye eat? Scott asked.

— Ih?

— Did ye huv oany money fir food?

— Wi stoapped it a wee bakers n, well, ivryhing wis rationed, ken. Well, wi goat twa buns, n Ah goat five Woodbine, cause Ah smoked like. A tuppence fir the Woodbines, n a tuppence fir the twa buns. Ah kept the money, fir it wis a long road ahead ih us, ken, ye hud tae keep so much. So! That wis an escapade wi hud

Scott looked at him. — Did ye tell folk ye wir gaun?

— Naw, wi jist went. Ma mum wis gaun aff ir nut, n Jimmy's mum wis wonderin where wi wir.

— So what did the say when ye goat back?

Wullie didn't seem to hear him. He was looking at young soldiers on the telly.

— Ah wis sixteen year auld, he said, — Jimmy wis seventeen, comin up fir eighteen. So, oanywi, that wis the end ih that. The war progressed n ... see, if ye wir absent fae the pit the used tae cry ye up, so we used tae work three shifts a week n things like that, ye ken. But bae the time the realised this, the war'd finished, n *then,* then the cried us up fir bein absentees. The sent Jimmy tae Gibraltar tae bore holes in rocks, is punishment like. N Ah ... Ah nivir goat tae go anywhere.

Wullie looked at the telly as Scott looked at his di.

A few minutes later, Calum got up and walked across the room to the cabinet, opened a drawer, and took out a white plastic box. Scott watched him carry it to the glass table, and glimpsed the pills it contained when his dad opened the lid, arranged in boxes marked with each day of the week.

— You need your nebuliser dad?

— Nah.

— You're a bit wheezy.

Wullie reached into his cardigan pocket for his brown puffer as Scott downed his bottle and Calum scrunched his Scotsman into a club.

Inhaling deeply, Wullie watched the fly Calum swatted crash land on the table. He didn't hear Scott's empty bottle rattle in the bin, or see the important people on the telly, arguing about the Middle East.

Scott grabbed another bottle from the fridge. The fly kicked and stopped.

King sitting at his window, swearing at passers by

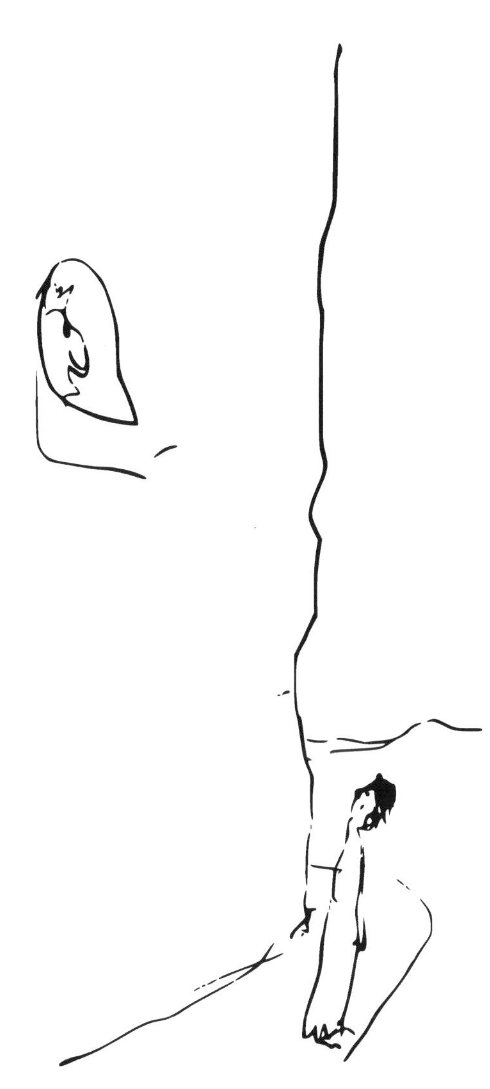

King sitting at his
window and waving
at passers by.

GIFFORD LIND

THE AULD GREY TOUN

Kings and queens came here to stay
Courts, processions had their day
King Malcolm worshipped Margaret's ways
The auld grey toun was changing.
Carnegie plundered stateside steel
To keep his mother's spinning wheel
A glen, a hall, a swimming pool
The auld grey toun was changing

Chorus

No more linen, no more mines
Or gable ends in crooked wynds
No more Kings to drink their wine
The auld grey toun was/is changing

Now Burgh, District, both have gone
The kingdom comes, a brand new throne
The provost's chain and gown have gone
The auld grey toun is changing
And Bruce's bones lie here today
The brave king's heart lies far away
Dunfermline's heart is here to stay
The auld grey toun is changing

Chorus

Each year sees changes coming round
New life soon fills this auld grey toun

The sovereign line keeps marching down
The auld grey toun is changing

Chorus × 2

Dunfermline has been my home for thirty years, and the birthplace of all my children. As an incomer I have been astonished at the part played by Dunfermline in the history of our land, and the extent of change that I have seen since moving here. Every year there is a children's gala when all the children of the town march down the High Street, pictured above, and play games in Pittencrieff Park. This was in my mind when writing the last verse.

ACROSS THE SCOTSWATER

We met the young Princess that married oor king by the
place that now carries her name
She worked for a land that had justice for all where the
poor should ne'er suffer again
And David her youngest he followed her cause made
laws that brought freedom tae life
Fae lands far away the pilgrims soon came across the
Scotswater tae Fife

Across the Scotswater tae Fife
Across the Scotswater tae Fife
Fae lands far away the pilgrims soon came
Across the Scotswater tae Fife

We left wi the heart o' a king who had fought for the
heart and the soul of our land
With his dying breath he had sworn us to fight and
crusade against infidel hands
And we marched and we fought 'till our valour ran out
and we lost many fine Scottish lives
I longed for the day when my boat would make way
across the Scotswater tae Fife

Across the . . .
I longed for the day when my boat would make way
Across the Scotswater tae Fife

Unless we forget, just let it be said that the heart and the
soul of oor land

Came frae a toun where the well trodden ground saw the
birth o what's now in our hands
And the powers that have passed intae auld reekie's halls
- a page in the book of our life
They came fae the toun where the auld book was written
across the Scotswater in Fife

Across the . . .
They came fae a toun where the auld book was written
Across the Scotswater in Fife

THE COAL DUST STILL MOVES IN THE SAND

The wee black lines that can be found in the sand along the Fife coast tell of the mining history that is largely gone from the area. This song reflects on some of the things that can be found in the East Neuk of Fife, and asks where next for East Neuk communities.

While the stones of the past wear away
Washed into sea
And the coal dust still moves in the sand
And the coal dust still moves in the sand

Where holy men lived in the caves
And churches and martyrs burned
Where Beaton first sailed to Mary's right hand
Where fights were fought and the ruins still stand
And the great wise men of old
That ran the land
Were left out in the cold
Were left out in the cold

I see in a moment that time has moved on
And summer's been put to the plough
And I stand in a land of forgotten dreams
And wonder where can it go now
And wonder where can it go now

Where the haar o the sea meets the land
Lookin out to the Bass and the May
Where the black boats once drifted with fish in the hold
A haven for oil skinned men of old
And fiery volcanoes once roared

Long before there was man
And the coal dust still moves in the sand
And the coal dust still moves in the sand

WAITING FOR THE CALM

This song is about a cave at Barnhill Point between Aberdour and Dalgety Bay on the Fife coast which is known locally as the Monk's Cave. The cave is man made, and was built in the 13th or 14th century probably as a waiting room for people travelling to the Abbey at Inchcolm, a small island where some of the remains of StColumba were buried – often referred to as the Iona of the East. The cave is now surrounded by Second World War gun placements, a golf course, and the Braefoot Bay Gas terminal – the cause of worry to many in the local community because of the explosion risks.

I've travelled far across this land
Trying to hold out a helping hand
I'm going to pray for my fellow man
And wait for the calm
I've passed some troubles on my way
Some will fade and some remain
Somewhere there will be some pain
Waiting for the calm

Chorus

Waiting for the storm to calm
Waiting for my boat to come
Waiting for the calm to return

Wind blows and the waves are high
Storm clouds are in the sky
I need a place that's warm and dry
To wait for the calm
So I'll climb to the holy cave
Sit and wonder at the waves

It's a place where I'll be safe
Waiting for the calm

Chorus

I watch the wind and watch the tide
Stormy water's not too wide
Peace lies on the other side
Out there when it's calm
Storm fades in the dead of night
I wake to the morning light
Holy island's in my sights
Out there in the calm
So I stand at the doorway now
Calm's here so I'm passing through
Now I know just what to do
Now it's calm

Chorus

Now this ancient resting place
Is closed in by the human race
The world wears a different face
Waiting for the calm
And wars have passed this way
The land still holds the scars today
And danger hides in Braefoot Bay
Waiting for the calm

Chorus

Repeat last line

CROSS OF LORRAINE

The Free French Navy was formed in Greenock when ships of the French Navy were mustered at the Tail of the Bank to sail on the Norwegian Campaign in 1940. It is often thought that the cross was put up to remember the sailors that died when the biggest French boat, the Maille Breze, *exploded and sank off Princes Pier on 30th April 1940. However this was not the case, and only the boats that joined the Free French Navy are mentioned. The memorial was unveiled in January 1946, and this song was played on* BBC TV's Reporting Scotland *in January 1996.*

At the Tail o the Bank up high on Lyle Hill
There's a peace to be found there, a freedom, a thrill
You can climb to Craig's Top and gaze out enthralled
At the sights of Argyll and the Clyde
The world that you'll find as you stand there alone
By a cross that's held high in an anchor of stone
Looking out on the river o'er hills and o'er homes
A world that's so precious to see

Cross on the hill looking out o'er the bay
To the coast of Argyll and the hills far away
To remember the sailors who passed by this way
And never returned to their home

That cross of Lorraine is for sailors that died
To win back their country, their freedom, their pride
A tribute from sailors of France that survived
Anchored up high on Lyle hill.
The words that were heard when the cross was unveiled
Were for justice and freedom and peace guaranteed
Liberté, egalité et fraternité

Vive la France, vive la paix, vive la paix.

Now can we remember those times in the past
The sadness and longing for peace that would last
And tears fill our hearts when each new day is cast
With more news of slaughter and war
And French test their bombs in the bright Southern seas
And fighting men hold onto power with such ease
The wars still continue – o where is that peace?
That justice and freedom could bring.

Monster

ELAINE RENTON

SKINT

The Credit Crunch, as we are calling this period of fiscal inconvenience, is nothing compared to the poverty that some families endured when I was a girl.

Take this boy I was at primary school with. He was called Richard White. Now most Richards are known as Big Dick or Tricky Dicky but this Richard was known, for a while, as Richturd.

Children are nasty little creatures. We all knew what White rhymed with and thinking back, I can remember that he smelt unpleasant, hence the nickname.

Now Richard was born just after his dad died. His mum went a bit mad and as Richard got older, so people told me, Mrs White was so unstable that she couldn't even hold down a job peeling spuds in the local chippie. She seemed to have no friends or family to give her a hand in any way and as a result the Whites suffered from spectacular deprivation. Forget the stock market fall; this was Skint with a capital S.

The Whites were so poor looking that it was wrong to call Richard rich anything so he eventually became known as just plain Turd.

Turd was destined for a hellish life right from the moment he entered this world five weeks early. He grew, but not much, into a sickly and spindly child. He wore National Health specs as thick as bottle bottoms with pink Elastoplast covering the lens over one eye.

Being mono-eyed he walked at a jaunty angle and was forever falling over. His knees were always in some horrible stage of scabbiness. His mum patched up the damage from his tumbles with old Elastoplast saved from his specs. Mrs White always had some dirty Elastoplast stuck onto a wooden ice-lolly stick and stowed in her handbag for these daily emergencies.

His healing scabs turned into the texture of beef ham fried for far too long. These were the scabs that Richard would pick at with his filthy nails, worrying around and around the perimeter of the scab and working inwards to the weeping and still raw epicentre.

When it was weather for shorts, I would sit in class and watch him picking and eating the scabs from his forever tender knees. Even although I knew it was coming I would cringe, waiting for Richard's sudden intake of breath as he whipped the scab off, ripping it from its small, oozing umbilical and popping it into his mouth.

He would glare over at me; one eye magnified to terrifying proportions behind the thick corrective lens and then study his raw knee. The gem of ruby red blood that appeared assured him of a snack in five or six day's time.

Richard White's clothes were even more legendary than his scab eating. Every summer, when the school went back after the holidays his mum would rake up enough money to go down to the Co-op and buy him a pair of Dunlop wellies and long, grey, woollen worsted trousers with an elasticated waist.

These two items of clothing would see him right through the winter. During the Easter holidays, his mum, who had become quite nifty at using scissors, cut the wellies down into smart, slip on shoes and his trousers into knee length shorts. As the weather became warmer Mrs White again showed her *haute couture* skills and shortened the shorts to an interesting length and fashioned the slip on shoes into natty sandals.

Turd never wore socks. To start with, his annual wellies must have given him a ring of sores around his skinny calves. As the rubber softened and the flock lining became swamp-like with sweat, each step he made produced a farting sound which endeared him to us even less. By spring his sores hardened into a thick black tide mark, visible under the hem of his Easter shorts.

It was the last straw when Richard arrived at school one sunny Monday morning wearing a hand knitted black balaclava. We had to corner him and remove the balaclava of course and we were not disappointed with what we found. His hair was cut right into the wood and purple stuff had been painted on his red scaly scalp.

He tried to pretend that his head didn't belong to him but he got thumped for having a new head anyway. After that we never, ever called him Richard.

SINGING FOR MY SUPPER

'SO THERE was this murderer walking across the moors with a wee boy and the wee boy looked around him and said. "It's awful dark and scary out here." The murderer looked down at the wee boy and said. "Spare a thought for me. I've got to walk back by myself!" Get it?'

The bus driver tilted his head back and roared with laughter. He stopped laughing very quickly, drew hard on his fag and looked at me.

'I like your shoes.'

It was a funny thing for a bus driver to say, funnier than the rotten jokes he had been telling me for the last five minutes. :

'They were my cousin's.' I looked down at the hated shoes. Brown and white wet-look leather. 'I have to wear them now.'

'Your cousin used to wear them?' He blew smoke from his nostrils,' and what does she look like?'

As I started to describe her the bus driver stood up, slid a window open and chucked his fag end out onto the grass verge. I thought we would get going but the driver settled down on the seat in front of me. He sat sideways, angled towards me with his skinny legs sprawled out in the aisle, leaning his shoulder on the next seat.

I was sitting in my favourite seat at the very back, right in the middle. When I got on the bus I thought I would have to make a bee-line for the seat. I needn't have worried, I was the only passenger.

'Right. Your cousin.'

I described her and the bus driver closed his eyes. He must have picked his plooks when he was younger because his skin was pitted with vicious little marks. He scratched at one of the pits under his cheekbone while I sat patiently. Earlier I asked him why we had stopped but he waved my question away like it was a midgie.

He loosened his tie. 'Did your cousin wear these shoes much?'

'I don't know.' I admitted.

It was roasting in the bus now as the sun soaked through the windows. The driver ran one hand over his face, round the back of his neck and under his collar. He was watching me through his sparse eyelashes and moved his head from side to side while massaging his neck. When he brought his hand down I could see the palm was slick with sweat.

'Let me see your shoes.' He demanded suddenly.

I looked at the hideous shoes then back at the driver. He had a trickle of sweat running from one eyebrow down to the side of his mouth. His pointy tongue darted out and stopped the bead of moisture in its tracks. I bent down to pull off one shoe and nearly jumped out of my skin.

'No! Keep them on and swing your legs up here.' He shouted.

He held out both hands and bent forward to catch my feet at the heels. I brought my legs up, a child obeying an adult's command.

He settled my legs along the length of his thighs and I kept my legs together primly just in case he saw my knickers. He was still holding the back of my heels and he pulled me closer until the soles of my cousin's old shoes were right up against the front of the trousers. I didn't like to tell him that the dusty soles were dirtying the material of his smart uniform.

The bus was parked under some trees. I could hear the breathing of the man in front of me and the twittering of birds outside. I wished that I was free, like the birds, out there in the dapples of sunlight.

The bus driver started to move back and forward against the soles of my shoes. His breath was coming out in loud 'huhs' and his lips were pulled back from his teeth as if he had a really sore bit somewhere.

A wee yellow and brown bird landed on a finger of fir itching at the window. He was so close that I could see flecks of green through the yellow feathers of his chest. He sang the same nine notes over and over again.

The driver pulled my feet tighter against the front of his trousers and I felt a big shiver go through him, right through the material of his trousers under my legs. Just then I remembered that the bird was called a yellow hammer and he was singing for his supper.

'A lit. . . tle bit of bread and no cheese.' I whispered, 'a lit. . . tle bit of bread and no cheese.'

Anne Mary Jesus Fish

GREG WHELAN

Winter

His death had brought you to your senses, like waking from a dream of falling or emerging from the deepest, darkest waters. Your first breath in years turned your body into something confident, your anger, drive and intent carrying you forwards like a marionette. Your bags, lying dormant and quiet beneath your bed, packed months before, now became a beacon; a steady, pulsing call. Merely moments after the funeral, your heart became attuned to its rhythm. It was then that you decided.

Finally, pausing for a moment before slamming the thin screen door, you opened your mouth to scream one last time, but in turning you had allowed your failing Mother to catch your gaze, where, determined, she held it. After what seemed like a lifetime, your mouth closed itself obediently, and with that, the last of your words sunk back into your bubbling stomach and were quickly eroded.

You had heard tales of other girls from the surrounding villages. There was money abroad. Lands of opportunity. New people, experiences, sights, smells, sounds, tastes. Though your bus-ride to the airport lasted a whole day and night, you sat awake the whole time, saying goodbye to the scenery as it passed, smiling.

You had never been in an airport before, and although small by most standards, its size was daunting. Having no flight previously booked, you were left no option but to spend your night there, taking notes from the cheapest travel guide you could find before eventually falling asleep on the bench, using your rucksack as a pillow and your duffel bag as a leg rest. After the janitor had woken you gruffly, it took a full hour to lose the dull ache in your neck.

Sitting by the window, you looked outwards. Soon, there were nothing but clouds and endless blue. At first you had liked the softly spoken man who sat next to you, but when he fell asleep on your shoulder, drooling, you had become uncomfortable. Then, when his hand gently rubbed your leg, you called the air hostess, and were shown to a new seat. She had looked at you apologetically but no more was said on the matter.

You landed soon after, and descending the steps, breathed in your first foreign air. Its familiarity was underwhelming. A small complaint.

Although treated rudely, you left the security checks smiling, and went to collect your baggage. You could not be reckless. *Bed. Job. Friends.* These priorities were underlined by the small amount of foreign notes folded neatly within your pocket. You exited the airport, focused.

Spring

Once again, the job would not be yours. The language was becoming a greater barrier everyday. In the hostel, it did not matter; there were other girls like you, and it was then that you were happiest, often proud of your confidence and strength. But every time you stepped outside, you became lost, and often missed home. It was a new and unsettling emotion.

Soon you became aware of the faces in the hostel changing from month to month, sometimes even week to week. It was hard to make genuine friends. Most girls had an understanding of language and culture. Some girls were prepared, learning long before crossing the seas. Some were less impulsive. You tell yourself you had no choice in your actions. It was consequence more than anything. Consequence.

Eventually, a job arose. It was outside the city, so the company provided a bus. You took this bus with another girl from the hostel. Her name is Anna. She is quiet but you are glad of the company. It is a forty-minute journey. When you reach the factory, you clock in with a special card, which also holds your name and nationality. From there, you move to the factory floor. The chickens move along the belts toward you, featherless and alien, their heads and feet removed. They are killed in another part of the building. Taking one at a time, you insert the blade in the lower part of the carcass, making a small, round incision. This is called the vent. You remove the vent, allowing the stomach to drop through the oval hole. Sometimes it is necessary to gently pull, being careful not to rupture the gall bladder. Next, you slide your hand fully up into its throat, the lack of diaphragm easing the action, both physically and emotionally. The remaining contents can then be scooped out in one motion, like so.

One time, when standing on the line, a chicken fitted over your arm like an evening glove, the round, mannish-looking woman to your left spoke. *What are yae daein here hen? A pretty wee hing like you shouldny be up ti hur nuts in guts, kin?* Then she laughed, so you smiled. You had no idea what was said, but it did not seem English. You could not be sure. You presumed she was foreign and smiled at her every day at work from then onwards. *Hiya Hen,* she would say. You are Hen. You are Hen and you gut the chickens.

You did not enjoy the work, but it granted you money, which in turn, granted other luxuries. Suddenly, you were able to have a life beyond the hostel and the factory.

Nights became a prominent part of your life as you began to enjoy the city. In the smoky rooms and halls of bars and clubs you began to enjoy the foreign men, playing games alongside the other girls from the hostel. For the first time in your life, you felt empowered, bending men to your whim, their wallets fluttering as they escorted you to the bar, their eyes wide and hungry. They would remain hungry, and you would laugh at them from the taxi as they stood on the kerb at closing time, registering you in a moment of anger and humiliation. Quickly forgetting, they would turn, their eyes scanning the drunken crowds.

Even these moments, however, were fleeting, and time and time again the majority of your friends moved on, hitching rides to the coasts where the promise of work was passed along telephone wires. You could not afford to follow them, you had to refrain from recklessness. You had a bed. A job.

Mere weeks later, you had less than that. Late, you ran for the bus, still dressed in heels and skirt. It passed you slowly, almost mockingly, moments before you had turned the final corner. As the bus laboured into the distance, you recognized Anna's face staring remorsefully from the back window.

But you found solace then, amongst the company of untrustworthy men, and the goods that they traded in. At first, you were uncomfortable, but that quickly changed; they made you more than you were, showering you with gifts: jewellery, clothes, alcohol. Soon though, you had realized it was to come with a price, and these men, in their satin shirts and deep colognes demanded the only currency that you could viably offer. On those nights, you shut your eyes and bit your lip, but refused to allow yourself to pray for home.

Drugs were being slowly passed around the round glass table, but you refused them, feeling drunk and sick in your own skin. All around you, the glamour was beginning to peel from the walls, melting through the cracks in the floorboards. Breathless, you stumbled through the bathroom door, cracking your jaw on the toilet seat as you fell. You awoke later, a man standing over you, urinating into the vicinity of the toilet bowl. Zipping up his fly, he stood for a second, sniffing roughly, before turning and leaving you on the sodden bathmat. You lay in your own sickness and stomach acid, crying harshly. Somewhere in the background, a husky sounding man was slurring your name with lecherous intent. Panicking, you raised yourself, carefully removing your Gucci heels, placing them side by side on top of the medicine cabinet. Then without turning back you opened the blacked-out window and jumped into the darkness.

On the fourth night at the new hostel, the girls asked where the scratches and marks that covered your legs had come from. The next morning you had woken up early and bought long pyjama trousers to wear to bed.

Thankfully, the English you had picked up through your experiences in the clubs and bars proved to be enough to carry you into new employment. You became a cleaner behind the scenes in a supermarket further out of the city where you were in and out long before the acknowledged staff would arrive. In and out. You preferred it to the chickens. In and out. It was early mornings, but you no longer went out at nights anyway. In and out.

You did not like the new hostel. You were up early enough to see the girls slowly peeling back to the hostel in their make-up or perfumes, passing you as you left for the night-time bus. The men that often escorted the women back sometimes leered and winked at you. *Fuckin wantin it Hen? Gee yeh wan, eh? Gee yeh summin ti smile aboot!* You kept your head down and continued walking. You no longer wore make-up or perfumes.

You spent almost all your time at work, or in the café beside the foodcourt. The girls at the hostel were neither rude nor unfriendly, but you disliked their company and the atmosphere.

You began to find excitement at your work. Soon there was a boy. He worked behind the till in the café. When you took your food to the end of the line, he would smile at you. Often he would try to speak, but you found yourself conscious of your awkward English, and just smiled meekly. He had shaggy hair and was often unshaved, but there was something about him that you found charming. His badge told you that he was STEVEN.

One embarrassing day, in moving to hand him the money that was in your hand, *one-pounds-sixty-five* counted precisely so that you would not have to linger for change, you became suddenly panicked and spilled the coins down onto the chequered floor tiles. Instantly, you became conscious of the groups of pensioners around you, staring as you swooped down upon the money like a vulture. Next they noticed the way in which STEVEN leaped across the counter to help you like a hero from a Hollywood film. *Awright,* he said. *Hello,* you replied.

Your days were becoming gradually brighter, and you awoke every morning looking forward to them. The only part of your life you still did not enjoy came in the transitions between the supermarket and the hostel. Your morning and night commuting hours still remained dark, and the hostel was not kindly situated. You spent your spare time in the café trying to discover hostels closer to the supermarket. STEVEN sometimes sat with you on his breaks, helping.

Summer

How long?

One? Two? Three?

You judge the days and nights by the shadow of the shopping trolley wheel, watching languidly as it crawls across the concave wall, its silhouette cast by a re-affirming brightness lying elusively on the left edge of your vision. *Outside,* you hoped, but you could not be sure.

At first you had tried to move your head, your neck, your eyes, your arms. Hopeless then, you cried inwardly, no breath escaping your lips or lungs. Eventually though you settled yourself, and remembering little of before, began trying to understand the present.

You were in shallow water, you knew that, its empty cold numbing your spine and the crooked, bloodied arm outstretched above you. But it was dark and you couldn't see much: the half of the upturned trolley decorated in moss and reeds, the slime-slung wall opposite, the inverted rubber of an old tire resting against your right ankle – strangely coloured.

Soon, time began to pass, your eyes adjusting slightly, and details slowly drifted into focus. Tiny things. Pieces of plastic bags. Tesco. Sainsburys. Lidl. A box, half-opened, spilling away from you, its contents unknown. Crates, and boxes, scattered, though almost organised, as if forming seats and tables. But what held your focus lay above these things: patterns and pictures and words, scattered across the wall in chalk and paint, sometimes scratched into the concrete – crude yet strangely beautiful in this place. *Faces. Car. Something sporty. Lion? Maybe panther. Or dog.* A multitude of female and male anatomy that although wildly incorrect, makes your skin shift uncomfortably. All run above and over sets of lines and curves. CUNT. PRICK. BAZZAS MAW HIZ A TEN FIT GASH. Words you presumed, but not in your language.

Your eyes, then, held little value, except perhaps to the rats that could sometimes be heard softly scuttling, their sounds magnified by the structure of your surroundings, becoming traffic, earthquakes, explosions … you couldn't allow your imagination to torture you. But there were other things you couldn't ignore, things too vivid to be false.

Outside, the world became more audibly alive than you could ever remember. A steady rush of water – a river perhaps. The sounds of insects and small animals. Occasionally, the bark of a dog. The rustle of foliage. And twice now, the steady rhythms of light summer rain. Apparently, although bloodied and gnawed, your ears still worked. Your right ear, however, lying half submerged in the fetid water of the tunnel, struggled and strained to catch the frequencies of such life. Soon though, they were plucked from the reverb of the tunnel, and then they could not be ignored, filling both your head and your heart.

Often, when the wheel's silhouette had reached its apex, you became certain that you could hear a distant bell. At first, you had assumed rescue, but those hopes had since left, and the bell then quickly changed, its ring becoming ethereal and something else altogether, another type of hope. And then there were voices. Beyond the light of the tunnel. Angelic and full of warmth and life and laughter. The smell of overpowering perfumes and aftershaves drifting by. Chortles and cheerful jeers. The shrieks of girls. Laughter from voices set to break and deepen. *Children,* you correctly guessed. And with that your hope was gone. You hoped never to be found the way you were. They did not deserve the weight of such a thing. Steadily, the voices drifted onwards, leaving you once again alone.

Four times you counted this occurrence, each time more conscious of the proximity of the voices than the last. However, now, on the fifth time, something was different: a set of voices remained outside of the tunnel, whispering quietly and nervously, edged with the anxiety of secrecy. Soon, steps could be heard. Gentle and soft, yet undeniably confident, edging ever closer, frustratingly skirting your peripherals. Your nostrils flare, suddenly invaded by a strong mix of aftershaves worn by those too young to know any better. Your body tenses. The rustle of the rusted trolley as it is brushed against. Splashes in the water and the slime. A small huddle of shadows to your left. Four at most.

A greasy splash of sludge skirts your legs as a trainer drops next to your left ankle. Then nothing. Silence for a second. And now, the whispering began again, only this time, its tone radically different. Hurried, yet calm. A gentle murmuring rises as a torchlight is cast, first on the ceiling, then slowly drifting down to reveal the brutal remainder of what you were.

You look into the eyes of four young boys as they stand huddled by your side, their faces dark, but their features obviously confused. Then seeing yourself for the first time, you suddenly become aware of your nudity; your soft summer dress, now dirty and ragged, hiked up above your chest, almost tied around your blackened neckline. Lying exposed by the children's torchlight, the paleness of your skin accentuates the gouges and scratches mapping your stomach, running south beyond your navel, the layers of crusted blood and dirt no longer distinguishable from each other. Your body is no longer yours.

An exclamation, followed quickly by a hushed yet angry reply. And then, nothing. The silence swells around you as you lay there, conscious of being studied. What you would give to be covered, or undiscovered, left alone as you had been in the days before, nothing more than debris; but all you may have had has been taken from you and you have nothing left to give.

Slowly, you become aware of the boy at the front edging closer to you. He has blonde hair, and even at his tender age, looks as if he was born to play sports. His jumper reads N-I-K-E-J-U-S-T-D-O-I-T. It means nothing to you. His trainers squeaking on the tunnel's filth, he edges ever closer. In his approach, the mask of darkness covering his face is gradually lifted, revealing a surprisingly soft complexion. He stops for a second, and you watch as his eyes trail from your feet, slowly moving up your body, resting for a second on your bruised and yellowed pelvis. Your skin crawls as flashes of pictureless memories, nothing more than senses or feelings or sounds, pierce your mind leaving you wanting to weep; but even that is beyond you now. His gaze lingers for a second, his breathing still and even, then continues climbing. You expect him to break his stare eventually, but soon his eyes, sad, beautiful and unblinking, meet yours. He holds your gaze resolutely and something inside you settles. Still holding your stare, he slowly lowers himself on all fours, and moving over your thighs, pauses a second. Sickness. Bile. Breathless cramps. But as you begin to feel the boy sliding your dress back down over your tender, broken body, the horrible tightness in your chest lifts. He has made you decent.

Quickly, he rises then, and turning to the other boys, shouts something in a fashion that belies his young age. The boys, previously gathered behind him, stop for a few last moments of inspection before quickly turning on their heels and exiting your vision. You hear the splashing of their trainers as they hurtle down the pipe, and then soon, nothing more. Steadily, the blonde boy moves to your right hand side, and sits himself atop a small plastic crate. Still gazing into your empty eyes, he gently grasps your right hand and squeezes it. And it is then that you know that you will no longer be alone, and that he will wait with you; wait until the sirens rise and you are carried home atop the waves, waves that push you steadily across the seas, until you are once again with your family, finally realizing that that is where you belonged.

A head in the forest

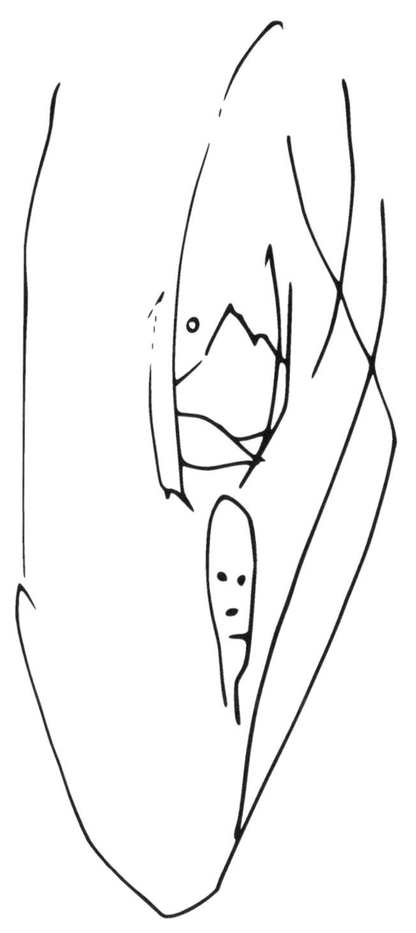

GAVIN FRANCIS

GREENLAND

ICE WAS SPRINKLED on the ocean like chalk crumbled over a mirror. From thirty thousand feet the monstrous icebergs were inconsequential, snapped off and drifting free from the glaciers which eased themselves through the corridors of mountains lining the coast.

The eastern coast of Greenland mocks attempts at description; it is sublime. The largest ice-cap in the world outside Antarctica flows out into the Atlantic under the pressure of its own unimaginable weight. The mountains that struggle out of the ice are dwarfed by it like pebbles in a mill-race, but from below they would have been seen to soar to over three thousand metres. Most of them are unclimbed and many are unnamed. The name given to these islands of rock in a sea of ice is *nunatak,* an Inuit word, reminding the West that Inuit peoples mastered these landscapes long before Europeans ever did.

The late evening sun was lowering, casting shadows from the peaks that stretched for kilometres across the ice in jagged silhouettes. The glaciers coiled and flowed between them in whorls. The same icebergs which had awed and inspired St Brendan one and a half millennia before lolled together in clusters on the edge of the ocean.

The aeroplane left the coast behind and rose over the dome of the ice-cap. The ice progressively submerged even the highest mountains, leaving only an immense expanse of unblemished snow. Something in witnessing such rare beauty seems to excite and inspire, knocking down the barriers between individuals and revealing a need to share experience. All down the aeroplane people grinned and laughed, swapped seats and binoculars with one another and called upon total strangers to come to their window and look out over the ice. Though we had flown three hours in silence, by the time we landed on the western coast the passengers were chattering together about the beauty of the country, the stories they had heard of it, and where they hoped to travel in Greenland, one of the last frontier lands on earth.

If Shetland was discovered through a quest for knowledge, the Faroe Islands on a pilgrimage for God, and Iceland in a drive for expansion, then Greenland was discovered in a last-gasp bid for survival. Eirik the Red was a murderer. He had slaughtered so many people in Iceland that if he did not find another land to live in, he would be killed himself. He did not really have any choice but to find a new world.

There had been clues about lands to the west. Since the days of seafaring monks in the 6th century there had persisted among the Irish the tradition of a great island to the west across the ocean. Called *Tir-na-n-Ingen,* or 'the Land of Virgins', the legend was reinforced by the stories of St Brendan's *Land of the Promise of the Saints.*

An Icelander called Are Mársson said he drifted to 'Great Ireland', where he had been baptised by chiefs in white garments. Though probably total fantasy, this island was said to be six days' sail west of Iceland and to be populated by Irishmen who had been living there for centuries. More credibly, a Norseman on his way to Iceland had been blown off course and seen some barren rocks sticking up through the fields of ice to the west. Eirik was not put off by the bleak picture that was painted of the islands, being no stranger to scraping his living in harsh circumstances. He had come to Iceland from Norway only a few years before as a fugitive, and had eked out a life on the poor and ice-ridden land that was all that was left unclaimed at the end of the tenth century. The murders he had committed there had been partly in self-defence, and so he was sentenced only to 'minor outlawry'. If he managed to stay alive for three years outside Iceland he would be safe to return.

He found the ice-clogged seas and the stony islands to the west of Iceland but continued on, rounding a cape in the south and then up the western coast of a new land where he found towering mountains backed by ice-caps, and a coastline slashed with deep and lush fjords. It was colder than Iceland, but further south and so enjoyed shorter winters and a less capricious climate. Out at the mouths of the fjords, banks of fog and mist rolled down over the ice-fields, but deep inside the valleys the summers were warm and the skies were clear. There were caribou and seals to hunt and green pasture for sheep and cattle. For a man used to the barrens of Iceland it was a rich country.

After three years exploring the coastline he had found two areas that seemed verdant enough to support the Norsemen's grazing economy. He called the whole place 'Greenland' and sailed for Iceland to rejoin his family and persuade others to join him in his New World.

In his absence Iceland had fallen on hard times. The soil was continuing to leach away, there had been another famine, and people gathered to hear about any opportunity to start anew. Contemporary accounts describe those lean years at the end of the tenth century:

> There was a winter of great calamity in the heathendom in Iceland.... Men ate ravens and foxes, and much ill fit to eat was eaten, while some had old folk and infants slain and cast over the cliffs. Then many men starved to death, while some took to stealing.

Twenty-five ships, between six hundred and a thousand people, loaded up their belongings and sailed for Greenland in the spring of 986. Times in Iceland must have been desperate. Only fourteen made it, the others being driven back or wrecked. Eleven ship-loads settled around the southern tip of the new land where Eirik had first come ashore, and the area was named the Østerbygd or 'the Eastern Settlement'. Three more adventurous chieftains continued on with their ships to the second area Eirik had found which lay further to the north. Its landscape was wilder, bleaker, more exposed and when settled it became the remotest outpost of European civilisation. Lying seven hundred kilometres further to the north and the west of the Østerbygd, it was called Vesterbygd or 'the Western Settlement'.

Santa Claus was bleached by the twenty-four hour sunlight. He announced the passengers' arrival in Greenland in Danish and English. The poster he was printed on was torn and ageing, the legacy of a tourism venture that was past its best. He looked out of place and out of season among the bare screes and scrublands of the fjord. Depending on your point of view the snows were either a few kilometres in towards the ice-cap or a few months away. Herds of caribou grazed on the far hillside in the midnight sunlight, and clouds of biting flies billowed like smoke around the heads of the runway workers. The air was very clear. Kangerlussuaq, or Søndre Strømfjord in colonial terms, is the gathering point of Greenland; all flights in and out of the country go through it. It lies about halfway down the western coast, tucked in close to the ice-cap, and was originally built as a military base. The Americans helped defend the North Atlantic from there while Denmark was occupied by Germany. They liked Greenland, and afterwards tried to buy it. Denmark refused, but in gratitude the Americans were allowed a concession: Thule Airbase, up at 77° north and only a few hundred kilometres from the North Pole.

At the turn of the twenty-first century Thule was still permanently staffed, and armed, by the Americans. Their determination to stay there is understandable; as occupiers they are only following an ancient Imperial tradition. Since Classical times the word Thule has been a symbol of the ultimate north, and the control of it has long been held to be the highest honour by those seeking domination in world affairs. In his *Georgics* Virgil wrote in praise of Caesar Augustus, 'whether you come as a god of the wide sea, and sailors pay reverence to your divine presence alone, farthest Thule obeys you.' Charles V of Spain too, when he sent his fleets to build an empire in the New World, had banners made declaring 'tibi serviat Ultima Thule', or 'Let Farthest Thule Obey You'.

This tradition has evidently inspired the empire-builders of the world right up to the modern day. The Americans look like they are there to stay. There are other permanent settlements in the world farther north than Thule Airbase in Greenland, but none of the others have nuclear weapons. The Greenlanders want them out. The Danes allow them to stay. It is another tension in their currently unhappy relationship.

There had been a strike at Kangerlussuaq among the baggage handlers. Greenland's population is so small and its communications so dependent on this one airport that a handful of men had held the country to ransom. Danish scout groups and tired businessmen slept on their suitcases in the small cafeteria. A smiling Greenlander reassured a bunch of yelling women that flights would soon be resumed. Outside on the terrace a few bored individuals sat leaking cigarette smoke and idly swatting mosquitoes. Children played on the swings, excited by the light and the lateness and the novelty of the place. Someone leaned over to tell me that the local airline, Grønlandsfly, is nicknamed by the locals 'Imigafly', best translated as 'Maybe Airways.' But then there was an announcement: the flight to Nuuk would leave shortly.

I gathered up my bags and ran out across the tarmac to the small aircraft. People who had been waiting to fly north for two days groaned and turned back to sleep. When the plane took off the sun, having never set, was already beginning to climb into the north-eastern sky.

Eirik the Red and his followers were emigrants. They were men and women who were unafraid, who had a vision of a better future, who were willing to work hard and who knew no other life than one of risk. Within a decade the new settlements were thriving. It was a rich country. The Norsemen had never seen such a profusion of seals, whales and game, and further north there were walrus, narwhal, beluga, and the greatest quarry of all: the polar bear.

They grew wealthy on trade in these rare commodities. Walrus tusk was a precious alternative to elephant ivory, European access to which was blocked at that time by the Islamic Empire. Narwhal tusk passed off as unicorn horn was a cure for all forms of pestilence, and polar bear furs were in demand for the hearths of the European super-rich.

To begin with, it was a good land to settle in, but the momentum of the migrants carried them on further across the ocean.

There are two sagas which describe the discovery of North America by the Greenlanders. One is called *Grœnlendinga saga,* 'The Saga of the Greenlanders', and the other is *Eiríks saga rauða,* 'The Saga of Eirik the Red'. Eirik's saga is more detailed but apparently less reliable, and seems to have been a later work more concerned with Christianising the legends of the Greenlanders. But it is surprising how much they agree.

It seems that Leif Eiriksson and then his family members did travel to a new land which lay to the south west of Greenland. He found grapes growing there which could be used to make wine, and so he called it 'Vínland'. In that country in the middle of winter there were still several hours of warm sunshine per day indicating just how far south it must have been.

The Norsemen did not count in hours, but used vague terms indicating the position of the sun as it wheeled through the sky. This means that the latitude of Vínland is unknown, and various scholars and historians have placed it in Labrador, Virginia, and almost everywhere on the eastern American seaboard in between. Wild berries similar to 'grapes' grew on trees, but not vines as far north as Maine in mediaeval times, and it is in Maine at an old Indian archaeological site that the astonishing find of a Norse coin minted in the 1070s has been made.

Leif did not stay in the new land after he found it; he had other things to do. He was a follower of the Norwegian king, a trader, and by some accounts, a man who had a woman in every port (he is known to have left a Hebridean noblewoman pregnant on his way from Greenland to Norway one summer). It was not for him to settle a land on the edge of the earth.

Leif's brother tried to go to Vínland after him but failed, then died back on his own farm in the Western Settlement in Greenland. His widow Gudrid then re-married, to an Icelander, and together they decided to make a third settlement attempt. It is this emigration by Gudrid and her new husband, Thorfinn Karlsefni (meaning 'the stuff a man is made of') that occupies most of the detail of the two sagas. Soon after the turn of the new millennium three ships and a hundred and forty people sailed west out of Greenland to start again in another New World.

Mist flowed down the Davis Strait out of the Arctic; dense and viscous, it clung to the sea and the earth. It had a ponderous weight, edging like dry ice smoke through the fjords which cut inland. With infinite patience it toppled over high mountains passes to fill the valleys that lay protected and sheltered nearer the ice-cap. Crimson and lilac light leached out of the northern horizon across the mountains. The fog was like a sea, waves of it lapped against the slopes, and it was drenched with the same soft pastel shades as the sky.

The aeroplane flew west first, to the settlement of Sisimiut. The staff of the airline were used to the effect this landscape had on new visitors. The hostess smiled indulgently as passengers hopped from one side of the plane to the other, marvelling at the light and the scenery. The pilot made an open invitation for passengers to go up to the cockpit and look out over the mountains. The landscape was astonishing not only for its beauty, but its enormity and emptiness. Glaciers dripped into majestic fjords which could have swallowed whole cities.

There are no roads outside the settlements in Greenland, all communications are by sea or air. Most settlements number only a few hundred people, and each has a small landing strip or heli-pad. They cluster around their harbours all down the western coast in the Scandinavian style, their buildings bright daubs of blue, yellow and red, vivid against the leaden shoreline and the pale backdrop of the ice-cap.

Sisimiut was a toy town, a splash of colour by the sea. It is less than two hundred miles from there to Baffin Island in Canada, and it may have been from the top of its mountains that a Norse Greenlander on a hunting trip first caught sight of the New World. Now it is a busy little port with a population of about five thousand – not very many in European terms, but in Greenland large enough to make it the country's second city. After landing there to unload some cargo the pilot turned south, following the liminal zone where mist banks of the Arctic roiled against the last mountains of Europe. Greenland is technically part of the American continental plate, but as a Danish outpost many of its ways are resolutely European.

The peaks of Baffin Island to the west lay obscured by the haze over the Davis Strait. Though the sun was rising into the morning, the speed at which we flew south caused it to set over the northern horizon behind us, and the colours on the landscape kaleidoscoped through pastel shades into the richer textures of oils. The horizon rose to meet us and the plane dropped onto the short landing strip of Nuuk, the modern town at the heart of the Norsemen's Western Settlement.

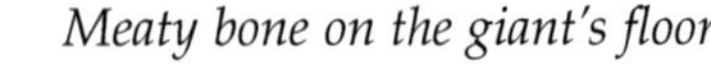

Meaty bone on the giant's floor

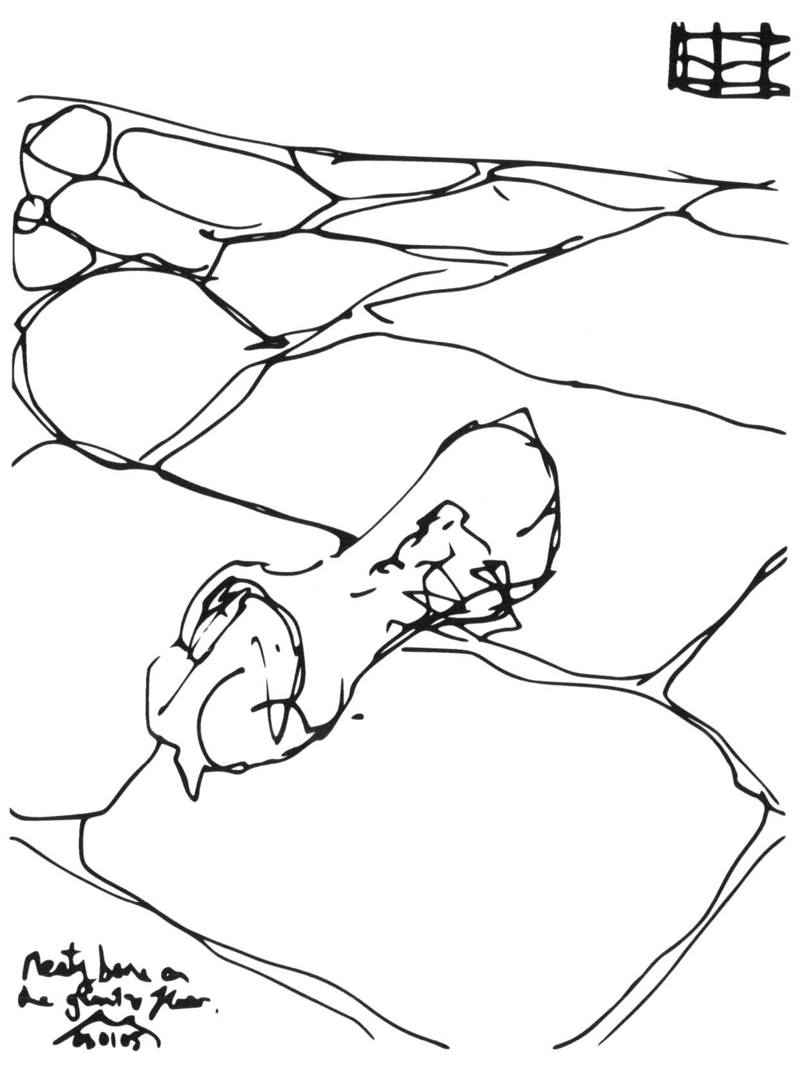
Meaty bone on
the granite floor.

DAVID SEAGRAVE

PEAL LOUD AND CLEAR, DUNFERMLINE BELLS!

THE AIRSHIP comes out of low scud and there below is a sheet of water with a track leading to a followable road into Dunfermline. We land beside a crumbling pier and set forth on our pedascooters. Runnacleave leads the way and we weave between saplings as we reach a sizable settlement, then we join a wider abandoned road, still with huge signs in the Precursors' language, English. At last we see the city of Dunfermline surrounded by dense stands of indigenous trees which have rooted everywhere, and some of them drip fruit that we dare not eat. Darracott brandishes a map of the city and talks about its history. It was once the capital of the Northern Kingdom, Scotland, and for some reason this promontory, Fife, was a kingdom in its own right. We have even spotted tradespeople's signs with titles such as Kingdom Windows on our ride.

The city is sited where a low ridge overlooking the Forth Floodplain ends at a gorge excavated by a turbulent stream flowing from the high moors to the north. On a cliff a holy-place called Dunfermline Abbey was built. The city grew along the ridge to the east and from it radiated roads, notably the ancient road to the Queen's Ferry at the Forth narrows where stand the three magnificent bridges that appear on the official badges of Fife. The map shows railroads and a station directly below the city centre on the line linking Lund with the eastern coast of Scotland. As we make our way along the remarkably intact city centre we deduce that it was abandoned quite late in the final years of the human epoch. Runnacleave says the last survivors congregated in an opulent house in a park. The oldest buildings of stone are restorable but nearly all the later buildings have collapsed, some of them blocking wide streets and they have spilt personal belongings in piles all covered with dense weeds.

We wander into the Abbey and find memorials to the sons of the city who perished in 'wars' that is the absurd mutual killing which was so much part of Precursor life (was it an inbuilt mechanism to restrain population?) and references to one Andrew Carnegie who was born nearby and who amassed the means to provide Dunfermline with its library and much else after doing things we cannot understand on the Empty Continents.

Runnacleave's wife leads the way up a flight of stone steps to the belfry tower. She invites Margaret and me to have a go, so, after a few attempts, we really enjoy our bell-ringing practice. The tower looks over the Forth plain gilded by late afternoon sun.

Darracot is transmitting our performance to Barport and Lund. Joyfully, God-affirmatively, Margaret and I as one greater light conjugal soul-stuff, affirming who we are to the empty city below our feet and the unthinking wind.

Peal loud and clear, Dunfermline Bells!

STILL THE RAIN BUCKETS DOWN ON COAL YARD LANE

I HAVE to be discreet when I catch kerb-crawlers. I must dress in fashionably tight metallic grey trousers, worn by the younger people, and the cowboy boots, also a one-piece rain garment and hood to protect me from the incessant rains. I must not forget my midge-mask! So, suitably anonymous, I say farewell to Constable Deepak Singh and hide myself in the man-high reynoldsia bushes that grow on ex-railway lands near Kings Cross Station. A good enough view of Coal Yard Lane where the whores loiter for wealthy clients.

It is uncomfortable here, with the midges swarming. I test my video camera with its image intensifier. There they go, the whores! All dressed in shimmer-tights and semi-translucent raincloaks, some with broad brimmed hats and they all stink of insect repellant like I must surely do!

Those Caribbean whores know how to attract men! Wham, hasn't she got a gorgeous figure! Tall too. At a guess, one ninety. How she wiggles her legs! She'll charge five hundred Euros per fuck! She paces to and fro as I film her....

The lunar colonists are emptying Europe's cities of whores, so I read. One enterprising Scot, Alan Ochiltree, is in the news for floating his Ochiltree Lunar Brothelage on the stock exchange! Will I, and other London Bobbies, be seconded to Tsiolkovskygrad on the Mare Serenitatis to, well, extirpate the nuisance and find somethiing to charge Ochiltree with? As that article in the dear old Thunderer stated, 'Demand always creates supply. Men will always want sexual pleasure 'til Judgement Day. Why shouldn't the Greater London Council licence the world's oldest trade?' A Dutch source says that Queen Beatrix is a frowsy old frump and our king has 'tendencies which must be held in check'. Insinuating that the king goes whorehunting on the continent.

A Rolls glides into Coal Yard Lane and I note it has no number plate. I take a still photo of the car with the Leica Noctilux and transmit it to Bow Street. Then I pounce.

The Caribbean whore has sidled up to the driver. I switch on the image-intensifier and brandish my warrant card. I declare, 'You are under arrest!' as I look at the driver.

Surely no! The high forehead, the RAF moustache, the penetrating blue eyes that appear on British Euro bank notes and coins. What am I going to say?

'I am sorry I troubled you, Your Majesty. Have a good party, Your Majesty,' I sputter as King William moves off with his prize and still the rain buckets down on Coal Yard Lane.

THE LIKES OF JOHN HIGGS

THE MANCHESTER-BOUND express pauses at Corchester Kirkgate and out I get into a bucketing downpour. On goes my hat and I feel so chilly after my long stay in torrid Arizona. Out of the station and into the welcoming streets of Corchester I go, to trip over a beggar as I head for the bus stance across the square. Yes, a beggar, here in respectable Corchester! And he calls my name chirpily, 'Mark Wenlock! Do you remember me, John Higgs, the cricket-captain!'

In a flash, a replay of our days at Grammar School. John Higgs in cricket whites dashing to and fro across the pitch, that memorable day when he hit a ball right out of the school grounds to strike a greenhouse and how time stood still after we heard the breaking glass. Then, recollections of him in the chemistry laboratory doing titrations and how he effortlessly translated the short stories of de Maupassant at sight.

The wind brings fragrances of Corveshire as I vacillate. Along comes a 37, so I say, 'Come along with me, John.' He gets up and we both stagger into the bus, I buy two singles to Prenticehill and I look at my old schoolpal, bearded, dirty and distressingly wrinkled for his age. Not turned fifty, he is wearing stained brown corduroy trousers, a pullover with holes in it and a raincoat whose sleeves are fraying. On his head, a woollen cap that, like the pullover, is holed and lets in the April rain.

I say I work for Boeing and I am one of the team testing their flying-wing airliner in the Arizona desert. It is powered by Rolls-Royce engines that burn renewable fuels. How come you, John, are reduced to begging? He does not answer.

Prenticehill. We alight and so to my trim home. A woman whispers something about me and shouts, 'You are not having him in our respectable street.' I retort, 'He's John Higgs, the cricketer!' as my wife dashes out to hug me, and there are my daughters ready to carry my luggage indoors. They all hug and kiss me and I am suddenly aware of Higgs' body odour and try to fathom out why the woman was angry. Then my wife orders my daughters indoors, frog-marches me inside and slams the door on Higgs.

'Mark, while you were away, Higgs was charged with, found guilty of and sentenced to three years in jail for sexually molesting schoolgirls. Yes, the Gospel bids us to love our neighbours and forgive sinners, but what would Jesus Christ have done with the likes of John Higgs?'

Bedragled fool

Bedraggled fowl.

30 10 03

JOHN MINGAY

ABSTRACTIONS FROM ALONG ANOTHER WAY

Abstract One

. . . and then,
for our achievements,
what happens to the timid?

There, caught by shadow,
we receive the twilight,
like living
outside the edges,
and are avidly devoured,

while those others,
who are starving
from being without voice,
become what we were
in the light of day.

Yet,
you would be anything,
if only you could dream –

you would be believed
if only you could know
what it is to be real
and be told what happens
happens through
no fault of your own.

But,
all too often,
we defer too easily,
immediately impotent
with our vulnerability
sweeping the shadow into light.

Abstract Two

Free from the symptoms of a will
that would have us think
we are our own excuse for being,
emotionally you find yourself alone
and sure of so little,
so full of the doubts and guilt
that have come to be
our only experience of the hours
when we struggled to be found.

And, alone, your life is in retreat
as you surrender to your fear,
never even trying to understand
that what lies between you and I
is a bridge to have us touch
what we remember – to have us
nurture the lizard on the cactus
that are no more – to have us
find something of ourselves in hope.

Abstract Three

And what we do
we do because
we have been betrayed
by our own synchronicity,
opened out for all to see

like a reality
that is free from boundaries,
free from dying.

And what we feel
we feel because
we are never as divine
as in our heart's dreams,
never as innocent
as we dare allow ourselves
to believe we are
and have always been.

And what we accomplish
we accomplish because
we have lost the will to believe
in the approval of others,
an approval we, for years,
learned to take as read,
but have come
to question as foolish worth.

Abstract Four

Perhaps this soul is rotten?

A mess of words on pages
that mirror an addiction
to a truth so seldom encountered?
A searching for sorrow
when there are delights to digest?

Yet, this soul, my soul, is not without love.

This soul, my soul is a door through which
our dreams we meet with laughter,
our happiness the very thing

that becomes clearer
by the day.

For to think it funny
is to be reminded that life
is only clay in need of form.

To shape life as comedy
is to make way for possibility,
all angles to be kept open,
willing us on.

That each of us
can sense this
is the point
where we become
on the way there.

And over time,
perhaps,
the silence will heal.

Abstract Five

Simplicity,
in human hands,
is the freedom
we deprive ourselves of,
blind as we are to how it really is,
bluntly, but slowly, replacing it
with more and more
of what we believe we need,
too much to hold on to
the next to nothing it is.

In short,
a suicide of sorts.

For we are dead to it,
dead to its invaluable answers
to the river of mystery
along which we flow
as fast as time itself,
and so attain little
of what our lives should be,
each day checked by
our snarling imagining
there is only dust to bite.

Abstract Six

We are those
who might just whisper the truth
others would choose to have
stunted, secret.

For your gospel flower
is the proof of all things found
and my vulnerability
is that of all things thought.

Alike in no way,
but, still, as one
in our hunger for faith,
we are those who might just . . .

Abstract Seven

To hear
a critical voice
is to hear
a straining stream,
a poem inspired,
leaps of faith expressed.

As with a song in mind,
you hear it
over and over,
as if meant
to keep going,
never to be final.

In a way,
the traces of ourselves
each of us
leaves out
creates a like-sense
of no choice but to let go.

Nothing we do
we have to,
must do,
and nothing is so soon
when there is no plan,
just future.

Abstract Eight

Too humiliating
is the art of loss
for the blunt intellectualism
that runs from the morning
as if from silence.

But, like a rite of passage,
it is an art of darker dreams
that become self-inflicted wounds.

It is a time passed through
when then meets now
and we sense ourselves
to have learned to yearn

all the better.

For it happens that with loss
comes a splendid, naked potential
that points the way to a new reality.
And, as each moment comes
of another moment going,
you and I, malnourished,
have turned to this, repeatedly,
as our kernel of truth.

Abstract Nine

Most things begin with either
fear of reality or fear of failure,
without seeing the connection.
Afraid of the future,
afraid of thinking –
but you are not alone,
you are only one of many.

Rooted by fear,
with no real cure.

I,
also,
meet my fears as you do;

not alone,
one of many.

Afraid.

Rooted by fear,
no real cure.

Unable to jump,

to run, to surrender to change
on the eve of success.

Lost.

Abstract Ten

We are shaped
by an energy
that flows through our pleasures
and by whether,
by how much, we resist it.

We are between
dreams like water
and a desert parched of joy.

Yet, being
what we are,
where we are,
we lack only a path
that is always sure,
a way that, finally,
may never emerge.

But still we don't turn back.

Abstract Eleven

We may find
the ruthless lies
of others
that have cost us
our appetite for truth
should be sustained,
but only

to keep the river running,
not by way of acceptance.

For the relationship
we have with the winds
will begin anew
in a language
strained, dictated by ritual,
choked by experience,
but, with each word,
we will come, all the more,
to own our lives, as we must.

Abstract Twelve

You voice
the taste of poison
the years past
still leave
on your every thought –

bitten once
too often
to forget –

your anger
takes to the road.

I, however,
take to my cave,
re-examining definitions,
learning the parameters,
the boundaries
of this darkness –

the next page slowly
beginning to unfold –

our two paths
born of one will.

Abstract Thirteen

With an end
there is still no final answer –

no shadow,
no shape,
no sacred tribe found.

We are by ourselves.

Alone.

We are the distance from home
travelling a winding path,
never straight,
but always our own.

Back

DEREK FYFE

THE SILENT SCREAM

As Mary strolls into the bedroom, she catches a glimpse of Ian. She pretends not to see him and heads towards the chest of drawers.

Jaws wide apart, teeth bared, face twisted in anguish, as soon as he spies her he relaxes and tries to look as normal as possible. Hopefully she hasn't seen him.

'Oh hello Ian, I wondered where you were. You'll be glad to be back home. Four weeks is a long time in a hospital bed, and I know you're not keen on hospital food. I'm just getting a clean pair of pyjamas for you. Are you ready for your bath?'

Silence is the loud reply.

'I've got the water just the way you like it.'

Clothing underarm, she pushes the 6ft 4in commuter around the single bed, past the computer table into the steamy bathroom. She peels off his bathrobe which is conveniently placed over the front of his body. Like a lump of fresh meat he sits in the slab-like chair as a big, bald, burly man with a black goatee beard and tattooed forearms quietly enters the room, pushing a hoist towards Ian.

'Hello Ian, how's it gaun pal? I see yous lot are third bottom o' the league again. Is it no aboot time ye supported a decent team fir a change?'

'We're gonnae gub yous loat oan Seturday, big man,' Ian replies, 'moan the boys! United we staaand!'

Mary smiles at the two of them as she straps up the passenger. Listening to their ping pong banter, she wonders why Ian never responds to her. Was it something she said? Even if he just spoke a couple of words it wouldn't be so bad. She was going to tell Sammy she'd stick it out for another month. She needed the money for Susie's wedding, but she deserved to be treated better than this.

There is a gentle *brrr* as Mary works the hoist and Steven guides it over the bath. Ian lowers inch by centimetre into the warm water.

'How's about me washin his hair the day, Mary doll?'

Ian scowls at him.

'Och well then, maybe no the day.'

Once Ian is semi-submerged, the harness is removed. Moist yellow sponges are generously foamed up with blue lagoon shower gel and liberally applied to his lower regions. They secretly catch each others eyes, knowing what's coming next: Ian is hyper-sensitive from nipple to crown of head.

Mary picks up the showerhead, turns it on, and slowly places it over Ian's head. When his hair is gently soaked, she very gently massages baby shampoo into the follicles.

'AAAAARGH!'

'Not long now Ian.'

'AAA . . . No! Stop!'

'Nearly there pal.'

Ian tries to hide his tears by sniffing them up his nose.

'A quick wash and we'll be there, okay Ian?'

Mary softly dabs his face, but he manages to keep quiet. She deliberately avoids touching the fresh scar on his throat and the metal plate behind it which now supports his weak neck muscles. The showerhead is switched off.

'That's it for another day Ian.'

She wipes her glasses. The plug is pulled. Soapy water slowly drains away. Luxurious bath towelling commences.

The daily routine of drying, nightwear dressing, clean nappy, administering of new catheter, hoisting, returning Ian back to bed, goes like tick-tock. Steve's shirt is saturated with sweat. Mary's white uniform shows little perspiration.

'Can Ah go noo Mary doll? Ah'm gaspin fir a fag.'

'Of course Steven, thanks pal, see you tomorrow.'

'See ye the morn Stovie heed,' Ian says.

'Aye, okay scarty drawers, see ye the morn.'

An intense silence lingers in the air for nearly five minutes as Mary calmly tidies up. Ian has too much time to think.

This is bloody hellish! God! Why did ye let this happen tae me? I was never a bad person. I never asked to be quadriplegic at twenty-five. Why do you hate me so much? You let murderers and paedophiles run the streets and here's me trapped in this dungeon for a body. One vertebrae lower and I would have had the use of my arms. Even that bitch of a wife took the bairn a week eftir the accident, and noo she's shackin' up wi her new boyfriend. SHE couldnae handle it! What aboot me? Emma's ma bairn as well. I'm gonnae claim custody. That will hurt her. I'll never forgive her fir that. It's no fair. You're supposed tae be a loving God. Even Christopher Reeve couldnae be cured and he wis a millionaire, so what chance have I got?

'I'm going to the church tonight Ian. There's a video of a woman called Joni Eareckson Tada. I've never heard of her before but she's supposed to be a very good minister. I'll let you know what I think of her tomorrow, if you like.'

Ian doesn't reply as she pulls the curtains shut and admires the beautiful flower painting above the bed, wondering how he manages to keep the brush in his mouth and still paint such lovely pictures.

'Rest well Ian, God bless.'

Mary puts away the suck and blow attachment for his computer, disconnects the Golf Game, notices he hasn't been on the Net, and turns it off. She doesn't notice the calendar above the PC with her words –

A FRIEND IS SOMEONE YOU CAN BE SILENT WITH.

She switches off the light and goes for a well-earned cup of tea. It is early afternoon but the room is dark once more.

Death trying to carry too many skulls at once

Death trying
to carry too
many skulls
at once.

SEAN HOWIE

FUNERAL

In memory of Jim Braid.

On this gentle slope into the fading light we stand
blackened people, mourning
a father, friend and Cupar son.

A fiery-haired minister stands over a shallow pit,
his unsteady Ulster brogue delivers prayer,
fleeting words,
flitting by weighted heads
like autumnal leaves in a breeze,
A man of God remembers a man of the people.

A black bird shuffles along a branch,
head dipped, tail feathers slightly askew,
watching this colossal seed being lowered into the ground.

Cupar's children are planted here
and in fertile soil they rest,
marked by weathered stone.
Forever cherished by some,
forgotten too soon by others:
Ranald John Machinver, died 18th July 1879,
Imogen Schulz, died 31st August 1984,
Patrick Sutherland, died 17th November 1961
this one I'm afraid I cannot read.

I thank the minister for His words,
pull-up my collar, bury hands in pockets
shuffling behind others

towards a tall rusty gate,
Gravel crackles and crunches under tyres behind me
Turning to meet my reflection in the passing hearse,
sobering thoughts grab me
as I walk away, I know I'm walking nearer.

Another jester, this time with his balls out

Another jester, this time with his balls out.

1840

RACHEL MARSH

WHEN THE WOMEN DISAPPEARED

IT TOOK several days for the men of Pitmidden to notice that the women had disappeared.

It was a new moon, and the sands upon the shore were tar black. For days prior, the herring danced the tango around the nets. The men stood on deck, dejected by the sea, looking out to the hills; golden lights flickered in the cottage windows, but the teasing herring kept the nets empty, and with no catch the bell was not sounded. The women were left to lie in their beds, and the men came to shore but made the company of ale, whiskey and gin.

The mid-summer dawn shone through the fog as the men finally wandered home from the Inn, and the golden lanterns were still lit in the family windows. The men respectively cast themselves upon the hearth floor, leaving the women to their beds. By mid day, the men rose, one by one, to notice that their wives were not in the house. The hearths tended to and the chickens fed, but the wives gone. Many assumed they were at the wash house, or perhaps market day had come early, but that evening the women still had not appeared. Houses were visited, husbands, uncles and brothers-in-laws consulted, but answers were not discovered.

On the second day, family members from beyond the village came to visit their widowed and spinstered relatives hoping for a warm welcome and an even warmer dinner. The men entered the homes to find their siblings, cousins, and aunts gone. They searched the shops, the sands and the village green. The town came to realise that it was not just the fishermen's wives who were away but all the women of Pitmidden were not to be found: old, young, married and widowed.

Pitmidden created search parties; they checked the roads, the fields, the woods, and they searched the sea. Not a single female, not even a little girl was discovered. The Elders assembled; by the end of the day the town asked the Minister to make an investigation. On the evening of the second day, the Minister announced that the Free Kirk had taken the females. He had no proof of the Free Kirk's presence in his small Presbyterian village, but the Minister never trusted the Brethren up the road. During his initial search for the women, he often heard rustling behind him, but when the he turned nothing was there except small fresh footprints in the dust. The Minister was aware of the Free Kirk's fondness for Isaiah 46:4, and saw this as a sign of their participation in the women's disappearance.

The Minister read a lot of Arthur Conan Doyle and understood the meaning of 'motive', and as he knelt at the alter praying for guidance he questioned the Free Kirk's motive for stealing Pitmidden's women. Just at that moment, a shadow was cast across the church floor. The Minister glanced up and out the window, but the strong summer light was blocked by the blacksmith crossing the kirkyard with bottle in hand. The Minister understood the kidnappers' reasoning; the captors wanted to save Pitmidden from itself. The women of the small village had allowed the devil's drink into the home, and, possibly, caroused while their husbands were out to sea. In the mind of the Minister, the Free Kirk had liberated Pitmidden from the sins of the fisherwives.

For the first time in his ecumenical career he agreed with the Free Kirk, but knew that, despite the reasons, stealing a village of women without warning was not very neighbourly. The Minister made preparations to walk to the next village in the morning. He would ask for the return of Pitmidden's heathen women.

The Minister took the long high-road to St Mornings, for the footpath along the coast was treacherous. He arrived by lunch and went straight to the church in that neighbouring sea town. He found a few Brethren whitewashing the church windowsills and asked for a meeting with the Elders of the church. The Brethren left and came back with many church members – both men and women – and asked the Minister of Pitmidden why he had come. The Minister explained that their women were missing, and he demanded that they be returned.

The villagers of St Mornings were confused; they said they had nothing to do with the loose women of Pitmidden. The men of St Mornings always averted their eyes at market when 'those' women passed – their ankles peaking brazenly from beneath hemlines. The women of St Mornings taught their daughters piety and shame, and would have never brought the women of Pitmidden into their homes – even to save their souls through captivity.

The Minister set out down the road for home, more confused than before. On the fourth day he announced to his village that the Free Kirk did not have their women, therefore the women must of have left of their own free will. It was also on this fourth day that the Minster was told that the dinners were still made, household accounts balanced, and children were tended. The men called a meeting to discuss the women. Where could half the population have gone?

The Elders debated, but eventually left it to the Minister to decide. He now believed it must be something bigger. The French Suffragists, they must have kidnapped all their women in the night. Sailed them to the Canadian wilderness.

The Minister was nervous. If he went to the neighbouring towns for help, it would make his village appear weak. This great place of strong and able fishermen had no need of women. All the household work was completed without the women. The young male babies tended to and everything in order. The unmarried Minister realised that the women had no real purpose; that the men were perfectly capable of managing their own affairs. He would let the women stay where they were. When nothing was done, the Suffragettes would let them go.

It was in the sixth night when the rape began. The rape of the weak and defenceless males and young boys. This was a cry against Our Lord, and something must be done. The Minister ordered the exile of any person involved in homosexuality, even if that person is forced against his will. Within two days, nearly the entire village was to be exiled. With the prospect of a completely empty village before him, he withdrew his order of exile and gave them all a good chastising.

On the tenth day, a young man approached an Elder asking for help. 'I am newly married. My young wife is pregnant, and the Midwife had said it would be a boy. What will happen to her if we do not search for her? What will become of the son she is carrying? What will the future of Pitmidden be if we have no women to produce us sons? What will become of us without Mothers?'

After the husband went to his Elder, they threatened the Minister by saying, 'If you don't do something, we will find someone who will.' The Minister then made an announcement, 'The women must be found!' If the small village were to have their women returned, a higher power would need to become involved. He made arrangements to take the news to Westminster.

The Lords scoffed, 'You are lucky. We have been unsuccessful at getting rid of our women.' The Commons laughed, 'They have probably gone to work in the city factories for more money.' The Minister knew he must go to the highest order, so he went to the King. The King was uninterested and almost dismissed the Minister, until the Queen stopped the Minister. 'Things have changed in our great Empire. I now get the vote. Not as a Queen, but as a woman. We shall find the women of Pitmidden.'

The King did love his wife, so he made a statement to the world, asking not for help – he did not want to appear weak – but insisting that if the women were not returned in twenty-four hours, the King would unleash the wrath of the mighty Empire upon those who had stolen their women.

The North American Christians got a bit edgy. They believed that the rapture had happened. But if it did, why had they themselves not been taken? Why only the women of Pitmidden? Had some been overlooked during the final days because they lived in the wrong part of the world, or because they followed a different denomination of the Bible? A lot of Mississippi residents suddenly declared themselves Scottish and added *Mac* to their surname.

Just before the twenty-four hour deadline, on the fifteenth day since the women went missing, the man who had gone to the Elder for help found an addition to his home. It was his newly born baby son. Healthy in his crib, swaddled and fat. He had been born safely and returned. The Elder reported this to the Minister, who then, in turn, sent a message to the King.

The King sat and pondered, and realised that the captors were not unreasonable. They would not return their women, but they would return their sons. He announced that this was an act of good faith, and he would give the kidnappers another twenty-four hours to return the women.

But the women never appeared. The King was never able to unleash the wrath of the Empire, because despite the help of countries all over the world, no one realised that the women had never been taken. The women of Pitmidden had simply become invisible.

Peasant

Peasant.

22.12.03

IAIN CRANFORD HUNTER

SERVANT

The crowned horse reared, neighed,
strained in every muscle, and bolted
from the stable;
from the manure-warm, manure-scented,
hay-sweet, humid wooden space,
from its cooped-up, dim, sometimes necessary
shelter.
It ran loose over the land, solitary,
strongly living, breathing well.

The vitality of the grass and dark forests,
the sun-song of the meadow-flowers,
the time going by, the hours
barely noticed; minutes don't count
nor seconds matter one bit
when there's a breath, a touch, something
that says, that tells you:
minerals, matter, cannot claim you,
nor coffins contain you,
time restrain you.

True life stays with us
wherever we stand or stray;
the mineral Earth is invisible, look:
sun and moon never leave
your sight, time vanishes;
though still you walk, will, think and feel,
still you churn the heavy soil,
follow the plough your crowned horse pulls,

sowing love in the dark clay furrows;

for no other reason
do we live.

DOUBLEGANGER

In bairnhood I knew not
the cynical face,
it was nowhere to be seen,
only the sun met my eyes,
shone there for me,
blossoming rose-pink and light, golden,
bright yellow.
Though the cynical face
and the dark, skelb-slender body attached
gracefully skirted around the sun-orb
surrounding me,
crept stealthily, cleverly,
waiting for a gap to appear,
for the first shadow to grow in me,
the first sunspot.

Adolescence drew near.

A sly dis-ease appeared in me.
One morning, in the light striking
a cold castle wall
I awoke
and for just a moment clapped eyes
on the cynical face for the first time.
It hit my heart like electricity then went,
had me doubting it lived somewhere around here,
in the human vicinity. It smirked.

Fire came; the adolescent flame grew,
torching the world; boldly I went

hammering society, laughing, chainmailed.
And full of fun one day
going jauntily along, rakish,
I turned a street corner,
and standing there, smirking at me
powerfully
was the cynical face
seven feet up,
atop a slender body of rotting wood
in a suit of crumbling, cobwebbed bark.
Ice flattened my flames.
Confident cleverness incarnate
towered over me;
I shrank in my good, child-like stupidity
or wisdom
(the sun still shone into my heart
every chance it got).

In adulthood I saw the cynical face
far more often, everywhere I went,
raising a glass ironically to me at a distance
in many dingy places in the city, smiling
sardonically, condescendingly,
contemptuously ; convincingly clever.
It haunted where I walked and sat and slept,
it was, where I was, and a terrible fear gripped me
through the years.

The sun was pale and veiled in sulphur.
But still in my heart it was everything and I.

Then lying in my coffin, cadaver-calm, corpse-composed,
all bone, and blood no more,
I still felt a shock
when I turned my head
to the side, and there beside me,
inexplicably,
was a mirror
and the cynical, cynical face,

smirking still,
and attached, the pair of eyes
that killed me.

Beyond the bones though -
home ; free -
in the sun, with the sun, with
the green grass endless like an emerald sea
and flowers of colours I'd never seen
below, I looked below
to see
the cynical face pathetic, subdued,
a weakly bully wanting pity
because around it grew
the sun
as sparkling diamond-seedlings in people.

ADVENT

The marrow yellow gold; the bone
a cracked open honey pot;
royal-jelly-rich limbs, a king's body,
the white ridges of rib-rows, femurs
and shins; the ridges of furrows raised,
blue-grey cold clay, glassy.
The golden-yellow sprout below in
the brown seed, asleep;
the bleeding ground, the filling hollows
of this season
opening the way clear, making a path.
He increases.

The honey running, spilling
like loosed sunlight, sluice opened,
and love spoiling for the bees,
the skeleton-skeps still in the making,
being built
by two or three pairs of hands
at least -
wax bones waxing, inside-out,
wisdom out in the open.
The common body,
the marrow-house,
human-family-home.

Shining honeycomb city,
Sun-wed.

MAY-DAY ASCENSION

Dead churches in spring came
looking for me, cowslip-ringed,
yew-shadowed Saxon stone-piles,
blown by a wolf-breath wind,
soaked inside by lily-scent
and saved from the grave by donations.
Coat on in the sun I circled,
then invaded the innards, the dead
historical viscera, stained-glass-lit,
a pelican pulpit pricking its breast,
a tree-beamed ceiling damp and cobwebbed.
The past prolonged, the future left
wanting for a way in: a baby obliged to prise open
cervix and vagina, causing apocalyptic pangs:
the fear of divinity being revealed.

Pierced feet upon clouds, brow up by the sun:
bye-bye, He says; the Comforter will be by
soon, will come;
welcome Her in.

(What the Seraphim and co showed me,
what was foreshadowed or had lamp-light
thrown upon it up ahead: time to come,
being to be, life to lead, life be led
the way he would lead it, tread the path,
the hard road, narrow dirt track, and
no turning round or returning, no column-of-salt
creating, go on.)

FORWARD

I was on a slow train, sitting alone,
and the knowledge came to me (the sight met me)
that angels had white wings not gold ones;
their figures were there before the inside me;
they had no feet, flitted footless, flew.

Spring repeated around me, leaf-patterned,
surging toward flowering in every inch,
as I travelled the metal tracks,
and thoughts went outside me,
escaped me, and became pictures
in the greenery, and in the empty carriage
of cold chairs, swept over with shadow;
in the bright leaves, sunny, my
thoughts lived, brought new growth,
never seen on earth, or heard,
or handled. Unusual flowers bloomed
to say the least, the littlest. And
I wondered if even the trees knew.

What grew there was grotesque or beautiful,
and talked, one being to another,
them to me, them to each other.
Creamy whites and shining yellows, magenta
tongues wagging, appearing and disappearing
among the common, veiny green,
and shadow-cold twigs. I wondered
if the flies knew. I felt sure the bees did.

Then blue angels filled the cloudless blue sky till the blue sky

was just angels and nothing else: moving together creatively,
surging like waves, winging, swimming,
in a surrounding way, listening to the moon at their backs,
following the words of the sun in front, doing its will,
acting in harmonious motion, praying.

The train slid along below: monotonous, linear, track-bound,
and sad, like a man dying who thought he was his body
and his body was him. He ran the risk of making this real.

But the angels ...

the spirit-blooms ...

A POEM ABOUT GARDENING

Like green in veins the leaves
breathe from the mud at my fingers;
I'll touch tenderly there, with secateurs
baited, held back, hooked, waiting.

It teaches me something the growing green,
how to please something, how to make happy
something I can't see, with my small actions
that anyone could do, though you need the Thumb.

Squeezbox worm going that way: what does he want
with the lawn? Where does he keep his brains? Eh
Charles? You studied him, you must know.

But Charles doesn't care anymore, not from where he is.
No cigar awaited him there. He discovered something big,
but tiny beside a mother's rhymes and tales to her child.
No, he doesn't give a toss from where he stands. Old hat
what he taught: 'why are they still talking about it?'

I care about a rose bush or two: guard it and clip it
where appropriate. It knows me like an old pet
and lets me.
Next one will too, even if we've never met,
even before I free it from a stand of weeds and it's
clapped eyes on me; even before we shake hands.
The green is genius. Something weaves in it.

Aye. Give me the Green Thumb

over and above the opposable one.
Cause the latter's no fun.
Give me the innocence of end-rhymes
and worms. And. . . , um. . . , thyme.

CLIMBING THROUGH WINDOWS

I am capable of seeing
windows onto secret groves
that no-one else knows about.
But I kid myself on that I'm not,
for the sake of a quiet life,
and to save myself trouble,
to skip the work,
and spare my fat horses.

I confine myself to the cool indoors,
to the comfortable and convenient shadows
where I can lie in peace,
potently idle,
undisturbed
in a broken sarcophagus,
in rotten, rank, mouldy repose,
ready to turn to dust
whenever they'll let me.

But the angels
are hard taskmasters,
making demands,
and I keep seeing these
windows –
flitting up into view
like shards of stained-glass.

What I see through them:
a sunshine that bleaches bone

and colours flower;
a heavenly heart with the brightness
and power
to make all earthly items
into flotsam
in a body
of light;

the flowers of the garden float;
the fence rocks back and forth;
the trellis of an angel-arch,
a mother-of-pearl portal,
decked with unreal roses,
drifts in the midst;
the path through it . . .
the light-sea path . . .
beckoning my spent corpse
to walk crumbling along it.

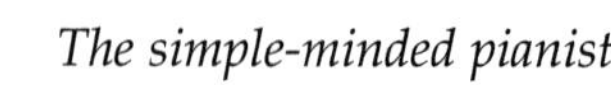

The simple-minded pianist

a single-minded pianist.

AMANDA FLEET

THE WRITER

THEY WERE gathering again.

'Not yet,' she said, gritting her teeth, 'I'm not ready for you yet.'

They didn't listen to her. She stared at them for a moment, wondering if she could block them or hide from them, but deep down she knew she was clutching at straws. She had no options. She sucked down a deep lungful.

'I haven't finished … the others … I'm not ready yet,' she argued.

The tall blond man shrugged.

'Not my fault. Maybe you should work faster.'

'But, James and Anna … I don't know if I can leave them yet.'

'James and Anna are just fine and have had more than enough of your time and attention. You've finished their story and you'll only spoil it if you keep on tweaking it. It's our turn now.'

He was starting to get tetchy. She squared her shoulders in defiance.

'Nick, I'm serious. I'm not ready for you.'

He clicked his tongue with annoyance.

'I've waited long enough. And that mist you keep trying to keep me penned into is cold.'

She still wanted to resist but the others were getting restless. Anyway, there was no putting the genie back in the bottle. Now that Nick had fought his way out from the mist, she knew that was it. Nick flicked his eyebrows up, his arms folded irritably across his chest. She sighed.

'I always knew you would be bossy and impatient. Okay. Your time. Your story.'

He nodded curtly.

'Well, evidently you know me. Oh, and my eyes are blue by the way. I know you've been havering over that. I gather I'm loosely based on someone you worked with once and thought was cute, but I think you should know that I have quite a few original quirks too, thanks all the same.'

Mmm, you're a heck of a lot bossier and more arrogant for a start, she thought.

'Yeah,' he said, holding her gaze, 'And this is Rachel of course. She's very upset about what you're about to do to her, to be honest.'

'I know. I'm sorry about that. But it's integral to the plot. If she didn't get cancer, you two wouldn't get back together again.'

'Actually, pretty much everyone is upset about what happens. Obviously Amy isn't happy that I'll have an affair and leave her, but Andrew's upset too. He really doesn't want his best friend to get so ill.'

There were waves of hostility coming off all of them, battering her backwards.

'We were all jogging along just fine until you decided to meddle,' snipped Amy.

No you weren't. Nick was already unhappy, the Writer thought.

Amy flinched and threw a glance at Nick who stared resolutely ahead. The Writer could see the edge of a blonde, curvy woman huddled against Nick, obviously overwhelmed by things. Poor Rachel. This story was going to be so tough on her.

'You know what, why don't we all just come in? I think we need to talk,' said Andrew, the tall, dark-haired artist who the Writer had always thought of as much more reticent.

'Not *quite* as quiet as you have imagined, no,' he continued, making her realise that knowing their thoughts wasn't the one-way process she had assumed it was. She would have to be vigilant.

They surged forwards en masse, mist boiling away from them as they jostled past her. Nick and Rachel sat on the sofa, Nick's beautiful brunette wife Amy took up a place on the seat next to the Writer and Andrew fetched a chair from the kitchen. The Writer's eyes were wide and she felt perplexed and on edge. This wasn't supposed to happen. They were all supposed to stay in her head; live their lives there, let her watch the tale unfold so she could write it down. They absolutely were not meant to come marching into her living room and start accosting her about the plot. She glanced around at them all. Amy still looked stung from the knowledge that her husband wasn't happy and was fiddling with her perfectly manicured nails; Rachel was sitting close to Nick, her eyes wide as she nibbled her bottom lip; Nick was stony-faced, glowering at the Writer, and Andrew's strong good looks were marred by a thunderous expression.

'We need to discuss the plot,' said Nick, the natural leader of the group, 'We've been talking about it, and none of us are happy about Rachel getting cancer.'

'But she has to,' said the Writer, distressed, 'I know it's tough Rachel, but if you don't, you won't see life so differently and Nick won't realise he married the wrong woman – sorry Amy – and Andrew won't have his friendship with you tested to the limit by you having an affair.'

'But we all know that now, so why do we have to go through it?' asked Rachel, her voice small, 'Nick and I could just get back together – sorry Amy – and Andrew could still feel quite challenged by the morality of it.'

'Or,' broke in Amy, 'We could all just go on as we are now and live happily ever after!'

'It's not that kind of book,' said the Writer.

'Anyway, if Nick stays with Amy we won't *all* live happily ever after. Nick and I won't be happy,' added Rachel, finding her voice a little.

'But at least then you two wouldn't have an affair, putting me in an invidious position,' said Andrew, 'You're my best friend and I love you dearly, but I don't think it's right for you to get off with Nick.'

'But he doesn't love Amy!'

An argument looked perilously close to breaking out between them all with no possibility of any winners.

'Guys! Guys! I understand your concerns, but the plot's fixed,' said the Writer, trying to retain some semblance of control over them all.

'Do I die at the end?' asked Rachel, her voice trembling.

All four gazes swung to the Writer making her almost panic as she remembered that the mind-reading worked both ways.

Too late. She had peeked at the thought and she could see that all of them knew the ending. Amy looked triumphant, but Nick and Rachel looked devastated and Andrew was furious.

'You mean, you put all of us, *all of us* through her being diagnosed, getting back with Nick, wrecking his marriage, then getting the all clear, but then you kill her?' he said, his dark eyes flashing with anger.

'It has more punch that way,' wheedled the Writer, 'And anyway guys, you're not real. It's just a story.'

'Not real? *Not real?* Oh, is that a fact?' said Nick standing up.

For a moment the Writer was jittery before she calmed herself, firm in her belief that they were all imaginary. When Nick grabbed her by the arm and dragged her to the laptop, her breath snatched into her chest with a small cry.

'Not real huh?' he said, propelling her into the office chair at her desk, 'Sit down. We have a different story for you to write. It's quite like the one you thought of, except Rachel doesn't get ill or die.'

Amy started to protest but Nick held his hand up.

'Amy, we all talked about this and you were outnumbered. I'm sorry.'

'Maybe she could write in you finding a gorgeous hunk and not being so upset about me and Nick,' said Rachel, trying to offer a consolation prize after she had bagged the jackpot.

'What about Andrew? What happens with you?' the Writer asked, looking over to him.

'Oh, my friendship will still get stretched to the limit by those two but we all cope in the end.'

'With what reason? I mean, if Rachel doesn't get cancer, how do you reconcile your moral objections? She and Nick would just be having a fling. The whole reason you come round is because of the fear she might die.'

Andrew shrugged. The Writer could tell that is wasn't sitting comfortably with him.

'And what triggers Nick and Rachel to get back together in the first place?' she persisted.

'We just do,' said Rachel.

The Writer sniffed disdainfully.

'So, you two get back together for no reason, Andrew forgives you for no reason and Amy just happens to find another gorgeous guy? Am I getting this straight?'

'Yep,' said Nick, pointing to the laptop, 'Now write.'

The Writer folded her arms obstinately.

'No. What you're suggesting is preposterous.'

'You don't really have a choice. We outnumber you significantly. So write.'

'This isn't a democracy. I call the shots here!'

'Really?'

This was too ridiculous, she thought. They had never been like this before.

'We won't leave until you write our story down,' said Rachel, 'None of us like your version.'

'This is absurd! You are fictional characters who live in my head. You are not flesh and bone and able to walk about. Get back into the mists. I told you at the start I wasn't ready for you yet.'

'You remember how much James and Anna drove you mad? Chattering and insisting you wrote at all times of the night and day to trap their story?' said Nick, silkily.

'Mmm hmm ... ' she said, wary.

'That's as nothing to what we will do. There were only two of them; there's four of us. And we're here. In your house.'

Nick settled back, his stare insolent, his arms crossed.

'That's what's troubling me. How come you're here? How come you're walking about and are able to shove me in a chair?'

'The power of thought,' he said, 'We've been trying to get your attention for so long now. We need our story heard.'

'Your story though. Not mine.'

'No. Your version is just too mean to Rachel and everyone loves Rachel.'

'I don't,' said Amy, 'She's had her claws in you forever.'

'I did have him first, if you recall,' said Rachel.

'And were stupid enough to break up with him.'

'Stop squabbling! Okay! I'll write your version, but where will it go? It won't get published.'

'It doesn't matter. It will be written and that's what counts. We just need to be trapped on paper and then we will leave you alone. We don't really care about whether our story is worth any money – we can't spend it. Once you've written our story down, we'll get back in your head.'

Andrew shifted uncomfortably.

'Actually, I don't know,' he said, 'It's quite nice out here and James and Anna have been complaining about the dark, now that you're not thinking about them so much. And you've always had a soft spot for me. Maybe I could stay?'

'You know, I *have* always had a soft-spot for you. Nick's maybe slightly better looking, but he can be a bit arrogant at times, whereas you are just wonderful,' said the Writer, smiling as Nick scowled, 'Maybe you can stay? *I* don't know. I never thought you could leave!'

'Could we get back to the point!? You write our story down and then when you have, we'll see if Andrew can stay.'

'I still don't think your version is as good,' she said, her fingers hesitating over the keyboard.

'And I still don't think you have much of a say.'

They started dictating and the Writer started typing. Their version of the story lacked the twists, the turns, the agony and the heart-breaks but she wrote it all down faithfully. After a couple of hours they took a break and the Writer made teas for everyone, taking the time to contemplate what was happening.

Nick had started out so nice, she thought. She really hadn't expected him to bully her like that. Of course, he loved Rachel and had realised he didn't love Amy and love does powerful things to you, but still. And Amy deserved better. She should create someone wonderful for her, to take away the pain of Nick's betrayal.

She let her eyes drift to Andrew. He *had* always been her favourite – quiet, principled, kind, generous – her ideal partner in fact. It would be delightful if he really could stay. How was that possible though?

As the others sat discussing the story the Writer became anxious. Was this going to keep on happening? Every time she had something less than perfect in store for a character, would they all rise up against her and demand a rewrite? What if she wanted to write about a murder and the killer turned on her? She shuddered. It didn't bear thinking about. This whole scenario was distressing.

Phrases flitted back to her: 'The power of thought' … 'Maybe you should work faster.' Writing exhausted her because she wrote as fast as she could to try and silence the characters in her head. She couldn't work any quicker so would they all start marching out impatiently? She couldn't bear it. Writing was what she did – designing all the twists and turns, creating intricate plots, weaving ideas together and pulling her readers' emotions in different directions. If all her stories got diluted this way, where did that leave her? She shook her head. No, it really didn't bear thinking about.

She became aware that the others were all looking at her and assumed they were waiting for her to start typing again. As she stood up, Andrew touched her back lightly.

'It's okay,' he said.

'Ever the one to soothe people, Andrew.'

'I try,' he replied and smiled.

'It would be nice if you could stay. I'm quite lonely sometimes and this ... ' she waved her hands, 'This is all quite unnerving.'

'I know. It's going to be okay. Don't worry,' he said and ushered her through.

They returned to the laptop for a marathon session that saw the completion of their story. As soon as the last words were down, Nick leaned over her and clicked on 'save'.

'Thank you,' he said, holding out his hand to take Rachel's, 'Thank you.'

Amy drew her jacket around her, eager to move to the next chapter and meet her new man. The Writer watched as they receded back into the mist. Andrew was still at her side.

'What now?' she asked him, 'What is there for me now? I can't write if you lot are always going to come out here and bully me into writing something I don't want to, and I'm a writer. I don't know what else to do.'

'It's okay,' he said softly, 'Really, it will be okay. It will all work out, you'll see. We were all thinking about it too and we know how you can write in peace and not be lonely.'

He held out his hand and she took it, questions in her eyes.

'The power of thought,' he said, and led her into the mist.

The jar of honey

THE JAR
OF HONEY

DAVID CRUICKSHANKS

HOME BY HERCULES

Shots crack shoulders back
The bee sting of adrenalin darts through your dormant belly

Flag draped half baked
Cinnamon and lavender splicing excited senses

Black bagged toe tagged
His smile floats towards you, a warm balloon homing in on the breeze

Sand soaked blood cloaked
Laughing at the prom, keen eyes sparkle shedding diamond shrapnel

Rocket fodder barked order
Whispered kisses spawn under a star spangled sky

...Frozen grasping throat rasping
Perfect union caressing the ripening grass on a dew laden lawn

Whoosh thu click boo...
Down the dusty lane necks and tongues nestle amongst salty tears

Scorched rock fear locked
Fingers slip away hands held up in hopeful waves

Armour checked pistol cocked.
His miles and hours clicking, oceans crossing, mercury
Rising. Hercules plunges down to his sandy womb while your
impotent hours crawl.

Cramped convoy Crackle contact

Then down the poppy trail
liquid armour flows

Sand sweat heat stroked
The telephone bristles betraying your heart while a
stranger in stripes frames the front yard porch

Dust clings storm clouds
A masquerade of hand shakes and smiles quell the blunt bitterness

Wake food shit helmet
Then rain soaked rifles bellow their mourning call

Sleep Hercules sleep
Frozen fingers clasp around cotton keepsakes while the new warm
blood flows through your ballooning belly.

Salome pole fishing

30 05 12

DEBBIE MACDONALD

TOY SOLDIER

Freetown, Sierre Leone, 1999

I sat at the side of the road, hugging my knees to my chest, staring at the mud just in front of me. I didn't dare look up. My friend Amadoo lay in the middle of the road, his arms and legs at funny angles, blood spreading out from underneath him. He was dead.

The soldier came near, his boots splattered with blood. I held my breath and wished him away. There was a scratch, then the sound of a match lighting. I could smell the ganja smoke. All around me people were screaming, soldiers shouting and laughing. I started to rock back and forward. Then I stopped myself: I had to stay still, be quiet and hope they didn't take any notice of me. I didn't understand why they hadn't chopped me already.

The soldier kicked my heel. 'Hey boy, you want a cigarette?' he said, waving a spliff under my chin. I shook my head quickly. I didn't know if not taking it was the right thing to do: I wanted to do the right thing so that he wouldn't kill me. It must have been OK because he laughed.

A jeep rolled by. There was a thud as it ran over Amadoo. I risked looking up. The soldiers in the jeep were cheering and waving their rifles. More jeeps came, one after another. Soon you couldn't tell that Amadoo had once been a human, once been my friend. He looked like the meat that is hung in the butcher's shop, raw and fatty. In all this time the soldier didn't move from my side. I thought he might shoot me in the head. I wouldn't have minded that too much, but I was scared of the machetes, scared they would chop off my arms like they were doing to the screaming people around me.

The soldier crouched down and tilted up my chin so I had to look at him. My heart was hammering inside me but I tried to keep my face still. The soldier's eyes were bloodshot and glassy; the way men get when they smoke the ganja.

'Hey boy,' he said, 'you want to hold a gun?' I shrugged – I was terrified of getting the answer wrong. The soldier hauled me to my feet and thrust the gun into my hand. I stood up straight and saluted him. He laughed. Other soldiers laughed as well. Some of them came up and slapped me on the back.

'Ok, good,' said the soldier. He grabbed me by the arm and lifted me onto the next jeep. Then he climbed in beside me and patted me on the leg. 'You're one of us now,' he said, handing me the spliff. The jeep rolled on towards the middle of Freetown. The soldier passed me a machete.

'Don't worry,' he said, 'it's easy.'

NOBODY'S BABY

My contractions started during dinner. A cramp jabbed at my insides as mother asked me to pass the roast beef. Silently, I prayed my waters wouldn't break. I smiled and passed the serving dish, the smell of gravy making me feel sick.

'How was school today?' she asked, her eyes narrowed, her smile fixed.

'OK,' I said, shovelling a mouthful of mashed potato into my mouth as my belly tightened again.

'What does that mean? Why can't you speak in sentences?'

'It was fine. Just an ordinary day.' I didn't understand why she had to know every detail of my life. Perhaps it was because she didn't really have one of her own.

'Why can't you just talk to me? Do I have to drag it out of you?'

I breathed out slowly as my belly relaxed. Under the table I ran my hand over the tiny bump, hidden under a baggy cardigan. 'I had maths first thing. Then drama. Then biology. Then lunch—'

'Where did you go for lunch?' she said. I wondered why everything had to sound like an accusation.

'Just the corner shop,' I said, as I looked up at the raised eyebrows. She was cutting the beef into precise little strips, her fingers tight on the cutlery, the veins on the back of her hands standing out like blue worms. She shook her head.

We didn't speak after that, the only sounds were the scraping of metal on plates, saliva mixing with food in a disgusting mash of lips and tongue. I hated her. I felt the thing move inside me and another contraction came, stronger this time.

'Please may I leave the table?' I said.

She glared at me. 'I'm not finished,' she said. I waited while the fibres in my womb coiled and relaxed, pressing into my back so that jolts of pain ran up my spine. The white tablecloth around my plate was specked with gravy: it would need washed later.

I waited till she finished eating, dabbed her mouth with her napkin and pushed herself away from the table. 'I'll load the dishwasher,' she said, 'why don't you go and study? You don't have long to go now. Exams next week.'

'I know, I know,' I said, getting up from the table.

I heard her go to bed just after midnight. She paused outside my bedroom door. 'Goodnight Louise,' she said.

'Goodnight Mum.'

I made my voice sound normal as I kneeled on the floor, my elbows on the bed, my body slick with sweat, pain racking through my belly and spine. I had to stay quiet. I had to stay quiet. I had to stay quiet.

When the urge came to push it was uncontrollable. I stuffed my duvet into my mouth to stifle the groans. I lay on old towels that I'd dug out of the laundry weeks before; I had to make sure there was no mess. Eventually, the thing slithered out of me. It made a squeaking noise. It was going to cry. I hauled it to my breast, shoving my nipple in its mouth. Its head jerked from side to side and then it settled down, sucking rhythmically. I grabbed the scissors and cut the cord.

Once the afterbirth was out, an exhausted calm washed over me. The baby was wrapped up and asleep on the bed. I knew what I had to do. Mother would be asleep. I grabbed the baby, tucking it under one arm.

I kissed her on the forehead, her skin soft and loose. It wasn't cold tonight: she would be all right. The street was empty. I scurried up to the hospital entrance, my hood pulled up tight so the CCTV camera wouldn't capture my face. The automatic doors slid open with a whoosh. Inside there was a flash of blue as a nurse turned into the corridor and walked through a swing door, her back to me, and her blonde ponytail swinging from side to side.

I lay my baby down on the ground, then turned my back on her and walked away. Beyond the car park was a clump of trees. I retreated into their shadows and watched the tiny bundle wriggle and kick. A faint cry carried in the wind; I had to stop myself going to her.

A woman approached from the left, her heels echoing like gunshots through the silence of the night. She stopped at the doorway, crouched down, picked the baby up. I turned around and hobbled home, trying to ignore the raw pain between my legs. I knew my baby was safe: I knew I had done the right thing. Besides, I didn't have a choice.

6 AM. I couldn't sleep. I wanted my baby. I stood at my window, my nails digging into the window-ledge, flakes of white paint splintering off. I didn't care about mother anymore; she could be as angry as she wanted to be. It didn't matter. Nothing mattered except getting my angel back.

I knew she would be OK, that the nurses would be looking after her. They would be wondering what kind of a mother could do such a thing, shaking their heads and looking down at my baby.

My breasts tingled; then there was a sharp pain. They seemed to be swelling and hardening. I touched them and thought of a tiny head, unbearably soft with hair like silk thread.

'Louise. Are you up? It's half past eight. You're going to be late.'

I stood in front of the mirror, my hands pressing on my vacant belly.

'Louise. For God's sake.' The door burst open and mother stood with her bottom lip pulled down so that I could see her teeth. 'What are you doing?' she said.

'I had a baby,' There. It was out now.

She laughed nervously, looking at my belly, looking at the discarded cardigan on the bed. 'Don't be silly. Come on, time for school.'

'I had a baby. Last night. And I left it.'

She shook her head, stepping into the room. 'What's wrong with you?' she said.

'I had a baby. And now she's gone. I left her at the hospital. Last night. When you were asleep.'

Then mother surprised me. Her face collapsed, all the hardness gone. She touched my hand, rubbing her thumb up and down my palm. 'Get dressed,' she said, 'we're going to get your baby.'

I grabbed my clothes, tugging them on, shoving my feet into trainers without undoing the laces. I ran down the stairs. We jumped in the car and mother drove, uncharacteristically fast, to the hospital. Tyres screeched; I held on tightly to the door-strap. All the time I could feel my baby getting nearer. It was as though a cord still connected us and I was desperately drawing myself in.

I was crying by the time we arrive at the hospital. At reception, the girl behind the desk gave me a sympathetic smile.

'Can I help?' she said.

My mother took a deep breath. 'My daughter ... ' she said, waving her hand in my direction. 'She had a baby last night.'

The girl looks confused.

'Um, she ... she left it here. At the hospital.'

'Hang on,' says the girl, picking up the telephone. She spoke quietly into the receiver, her back turned to us. 'Someone's coming,' she said as she put the receiver back in its cradle, 'would you please take a seat in the waiting area'.

As we sat and waited, my longing became unbearable: my whole body ached for my girl. I decided then that I would call her Sophie.

Eventually a stern looking woman walked purposefully towards us. I knew I was in trouble, but I didn't care. I just wanted my baby.

'Where is she?' I said, getting to my feet.

'Please come with me,' she said, her eyes locked on mine.

'I'm sorry,' I said, 'I ... I don't know why I did it.'

She guided me by the elbow, her hand cool and dry, taking us into a small room with plastic chairs and thin curtains with a teddy bear pattern printed on them.

'I'm not sure what this is about,' she said.

'It's about the baby. I'm its mother,' I said to her. 'I'm sorry. I panicked. I'm sorry but I just ... I just want my baby.' I couldn't bear it a minute longer; I had to hold her in my arms.

The woman turns to my mother. 'One of our psychiatrists is on his way down,' she said quietly.

'I don't need a psychiatrist,' I screamed at her. 'Where's my baby? Where is she?'

'I'm sorry dear,' said the woman, 'but there is no baby. There was no baby abandoned here last night.'

My mother's mouth tightened, her eyes turned on me.

'The CCTV,' I said, 'look at the CCTV. You'll see me. I've got my hood up. I put her outside the door at A and E. About two o'clock. And then a woman came. She picked her up. She must have taken her in. She must have given her to a nurse to look after.'

'I'm sorry,' said the woman, glancing at the door as a man in a white coat walked in. 'I'm sorry,' she said, 'the CCTV isn't working. But no-one came in here with a baby last night.'

I shook my head, backing into the wall. Slowly I slid down, covering my face with my hands. Arms grabbed me, gently pulling me to my feet. 'It's ok,' they said 'don't worry, it'll be all right.' But I knew with certainty, even then, that it wasn't true.

GARDEN OF EDEN

MY NAME is Louis Wavamu. I have travelled five thousand miles to be here: all I want is a chance. My beautiful wife Ella, with her skin that shines like wet chocolate, stays at home with my four-year-old daughter, Mary. I love my home. It is a tiny village, deep in the bush of the Congo – a wonderful place full of banana trees, coconut palm and African cedar. It is alive with monkeys, snakes and okapis. Truly, it could be the Garden of Eden.

But we never know when the rebels will come: they have been close before. I am scared of the rebels and what they will do to Ella and Mary. And me, yes I admit it I am afraid for myself as well.

That is why I am here, in Scotland. I must make money, enough money to send for Ella and Mary. We would be safe here – safe and happy. And I would work hard, pay my tax money, bring up Mary to be a good citizen, a pride to her country. We would live quietly and be good neighbours.

No. I must go home. They say I am not allowed to stay, my case is not good enough. I must go home. I am ashamed to go home to Ella and Mary. I must tell them I have failed.

Excited Ghoul

excited
ghoul.

21.1.03

ANDREW FERGUSON

READY TO GO IN GLENROTHES

THE BALD MAN was staring at him again in the vegetable aisle at Morrison's.

'It's you, isn't it?'

'Who?' Donald said. The man was familiar. He had worked with him in the Development Corporation. He ...

'Donald Sproule.' The bald man had been peering at him, but now he was frowning. 'I thought you were dead.'

The two men's trolleys were out of alignment between the carrots and the onions. People were tutting now and taking the long way round the potato island. Donald felt his heartrate quicken. He still couldn't remember who the man was, exactly, but he remembered he didn't like him.

It was out before he had time to think.

'Maybe I am, then,' he said. 'Dead, I mean. Did you ever think of that?' Pushing his trolley forward towards the next aisle, he dunted the other man's in the process. When he looked back, he saw the man was still staring at him, wide-eyed.

Donald remembered the name when he was putting the bags in the car. Tom Drysdale. He was in Engineers, or Architects, one of the two. Donald had had to convene a disciplinary about some stand-up barney Drysdale had had with his boss.

He couldn't be sure Drysdale had been responsible for the crank calls made to his home number for some weeks after the disciplinary, but he was the most likely suspect. Dorothy had used the calls as an excuse to double the amount of sleeping pills she was popping at the time.

When he got home, he remembered he'd forgotten the potatoes.

'Can't you remember anything?' Dorothy said. Or do you just not listen to a word I say?'

'Not if I can help it,' he muttered, when he was on her deaf side.

Drysdale was in Morrison's again when Donald did his next weekly shop. He saw Donald, and looked away, quickly. Donald found himself smiling suddenly, and gripped the trolley handle more tightly. He began to stalk the other man as he entered the butchery department. Donald felt a pressure building inside him, a devilment born of years of frustration, dealing with people like Drysdale, dealing with Dorothy.

Still, what happened next surprised him. He waited till the other shoppers had drifted away from the chicken display Drysdale was at. The bald man's head gleamed in the artificial brightness as he mulled over drumsticks or thighs. Donald edged closer, his trolley running true as an arrow for once.

'Wooooohhh! I'm a spirit body!' he said, into Drysdale's hairy ear.

The effect was electric. Drysdale spun round, saw Donald, and reversed his trolley so fast it set off an avalanche of chicken pieces in the chiller cabinet. He disappeared off round the next corner like a startled wildebeest, making an odd, whinnying, noise.

Donald's heart rate went into overdrive, then, but slowed gradually as he left the bright lights of butchery for the calmer shores of Pulses, Pastas and Rice. Drysdale's trolley, abandoned like a convenience store *Marie Celeste,* was in the next aisle.

Three days later the *In Deepest Sympathy* card dropped through the door.

'What's this?' said Dorothy, slitting the envelope suspiciously. She always got to the mail first, no matter how early he lay in wait for it. Donald pretended to be interested in *The Scotsman.*

She scanned the card inside. 'Tom and Margaret Drysdale? So sorry for your recent bereavement, Donald was a fine man? Do we know them? They think you're dead, Donald. How can they think that?' He could hear her thinking in the silence.

'You're not dead, are you?'

Donald sighed. It would take too long to explain. 'They must've got me mixed up with someone else.'

Dorothy's eyes bored into him through the newspaper. Somehow, he thought to himself, she would find a way of making the whole thing his fault.

By the time he went back again to Morrison's, three more cards from ex-Corporation colleagues had appeared. News of his demise seemed to be spreading. At the supermarket, he noticed a couple of people he half-knew giving him funny looks. No sign of Drysdale, however.

When he got back home, Dorothy had managed to get a joiner out to change the locks. A *Glenrothes Gazette* flopped out through the letterbox. The flap opened again and he saw her looking out at him.

'Go away, Donald. You're dead,' she said, her voice rising. 'There's an obituary in the paper about you so you must be dead. All my friends have been phoning me, you know. I don't want to live with a corpse!'

'But I'm not dead!' he shouted. 'It's just a stupid prank gone wrong, Dorothy. It's that bastard Drysdale: he must've put the death notice in the paper.'

But the letterbox stayed shut. Eventually, Donald stopped knocking and went back to the car. He sat a while, and let Classic FM wash over him. At least I've got the car, he thought. And the shopping, for that matter. He decided to drive round and have coffee with their mutual friend, Betty, until things settled down a bit with Dorothy.

But Betty answered the door with that same strange look in her eye as the folk in the supermarket. 'Donald. I . . . eh . . . I was just reading about you in the Gazette. It said you had — '

'Died? Do I look dead?'

Betty stood with her mouth open, clearly undecided on the issue. Donald drew a deep breath. 'Well, fine then. Let me in for a cup of coffee or I'll eat your brains.'

As Betty rattled the coffee cups in the kitchen, Donald sat in the living room and felt his mind's paradigms shift. What was it that management guru had said at the seminar all those years ago? *The three stroke cycle: plan, perform, review.*

Well, he hadn't planned any of this, but maybe now was the time to review. As Betty came through with the tray, Donald noticed, not for the first time, what a good sized room this was. There was just his friend in the whole place now, since she'd lost George last year.

'Betty,' he said, sipping the milky coffee. 'How would you fancy having a lodger?'

And so Donald Sproule's strange living death in Glenrothes began. It wasn't all plain sailing, of course. Betty reluctantly agreed to take him to the memorial service in heavy disguise. But the minister – whom he had never met, being a non-churchgoer – was so inept that Donald stood up to heckle, and succeeded in being possibly the only person to be evicted from his own funeral whilst wearing a false moustache.

Other moves came off a little better. He managed to empty the joint accounts before Dorothy thought of informing the bank. Then, after a spot of night-time bin-diving in Tom Drysdale's paper recycling, he opened an account in his enemy's name, draining the real Tom Drysdale's funds dry over a period of a month with a series of strategically phased withdrawals.

The only fly in the ointment was that his pension had stopped. He considered a number of employment opportunities before going for the only one that seemed to make sense: collecting trolleys at Morrison's.

'We don't discriminate against dead people here,' the store manager told him, with a hint of corporate pride.

Sproule found he could access a range of public services easily enough, but that, being dead, he was no longer subject to the other sure thing: taxes. And Glenrothes, so often criticised for a lack of community spirit, rallied round their recently deceased fellow citizen. Having a resident zombie might not be much of a claim to fame, but it was more than Kirkcaldy could manage, at least.

He saw Dorothy at Morrison's, once: she tried to speak to him, but was ushered away by the protective band of Goth skateboarders who looked out for him these days. He smiled at her, waved as she disappeared behind a wall of black.

Things had a way of sorting themselves out, he thought, coupling a train of shopping trolleys and getting ready to roll.

AUTHORS' BIOGRAPHIES

Glenn Gates

Glenn Gates was born in a Fife town and grew up in one of the West Fife villages during the demise of coal. Feeling marginalised from a very early age, he left as soon as he could to enjoy city culture. Returning to his roots after many years on an ill-conceived whim, he found himself in a society that had become alien and hostile to someone of his kind. Broke and trapped, he has never resigned himself to this new but temporary fate.

Daniel Kalder

Daniel Kalder was born in Scotland in 1974. For ten years he lived in the former Soviet Union applying himself to various trades, although he never sold arms or human organs. He currently resides in Texas.

Major publications: *Strange Telescopes* (Faber & Faber), *Lost Cosmonaut* (Faber & Faber).

www.danielkalder.com

Dr Robert Stark

Robert Stark is currently writing about his experiences in Lebanon, where he is Assistant Professor of English at the University of Balamand.

jargoner@gmail.com

Additional note: 'Queen of the Haugh' was first published in the inaugural issue of *The New Hampshire Review.*

Iain Bahlaj

Iain Bahlaj: lives in Lochgelly, works as night-shift manager in shop. One novel published, few short stories, play sent to Traverse, TV script in progress.

Ross Wilson

Ross Wilson was born in Dunfermline in 1978 and raised in Kelty. A Hawthornden Fellow in 2004, his fiction and poetry has appeared in many literary magazines and anthologies, including *Edinburgh Review, New Writing Scotland,* and the *Macallan Shorts* (Polygon).

www.wetink.wetpaint.com

Gifford Lind

Gifford Lind was born in Irvine, grew up in Greenock, and has lived in Dunfermline for more than half his life. He started singing as he learned to talk, inspired by his mother's enthusiasm for music and song. In the late 1980s he decided to try his hand at playing guitar and learn some folk songs, and this led to a growing desire to write and perform his own songs, and a longstanding involvement with the Dunfermline Folk Club. He has performed at events throughout Fife, in other parts of Scotland and in Ireland, Norway and Germany. He was instrumental in establishing The New Makars Trust which supports the development and performance of songs about life in Scottish communities, and has directed all the Trust's projects in Fife.

In 1996 he collaborated with Alex Mackenzie to produce an album *Different Places – Different Times.* This was given limited circulation and has now sold out. Tracks were played on Radio Scotland, and one of the songs – 'Cross of Lorraine' – was played on BBC Scotland's Reporting Scotland on the 50th anniversary of the cross being placed at the top of the Lyle Hill behind Greenock.

www.giffordlind.com

Elaine Renton

Elaine Renton feels that 2009 has been the year of *her* homecoming and has had five of her short stories published. Originally from Falkirk, Elaine's life has been so full of incident, colour and variety that she doesn't have to look far for inspiration. Now settled in rural St. Andrews, Elaine has discovered the writer within her.

Greg Whelan

Greg Whelan is twenty-two and hails from Methil, Fife. He is enrolled in the MSc Creative Writing program at Edinburgh University, from which he previously graduated in June 2009 with an MA Hons in English Literature. He is currently working on several projects and may be contacted on:

fengphooie@msn.com

Gavin Francis

Gavin Francis was brought up in Carnock, went to Queen Anne High School in Dunfermline, and now lives in Orkney. He has travelled widely on all seven continents, lived for a year on an Antarctic base, and together with his wife spent eighteen months driving a motorbike from Scotland to New Zealand. He has worked as a travel writer for the Sunday Herald, and in 2008 published *True North – Travels in Arctic Europe* with Birlinn Polygon. It is a travel book written about a journey through Shetland, Faroe, Iceland, Greenland, Svalbard and Lapland. For this anthology he has chosen an excerpt from *True North* describing his arrival in Greenland.

www.gavinfrancis.com

David Seagrave

David Seagrave was born in 1941, moulded by Red Hill Remedial School and severely scathed by a Christian upbringing. The outcome being that he created a kind of alter ego known as The Socrates of Charford who invents a code of behaviour, better than Christian morality, and struggles to live according to it's teachings. David plays Plato to Alan Wright's Socrates. His most earnest ambition is to have at least four novels published.

Whilst he produced a school magazine, his literary output became a torrent after being maimed in 1981. He has been known to write three short stories in two hours! His period cottage near Dunfermline is being crammed to capacity with his literary works, art photographs and model railways built deliberately from recycled materials. He is the only railway modeller in Dunfermline and the only man to build such elaborate models from all kinds of miscellaneous objects.

His highly controversial and often wickedly funny stories mirror the lifelong torments and irrational guilt which his late father imparted to him. He could not face the bondage of marriage, so his literary works are his abiding legacy to mankind.

John Mingay

Born and raised in Paisley, Renfrewshire, John Mingay has been managing editor of internationally acclaimed Raunchland Publications (*www.raunchland.co.uk*) since 1984 and now, following several years as Writer-in-Residence and Writer-in-the-Community in Darlington, Co. Durham, during which time, amongst other collaborative and individual projects, he tutored widely in creative writing and had three plays produced by local touring companies, lives in Dunfermline, Scotland , where he continues to write poetry and plays. In addition, he was editor of *3×4* magazine, 1989–95, and the Lung Gom Press, 1995-97, and has been widely published in international literary magazines, web journals, anthologies, collaborative projects and in over forty individual collections over the last twenty-five years. From 1990 to 2000 he worked in community arts development in West Fife. His recent plays are currently attracting attention in Spain, with *Los Caprichos* in production with Saltarrana Teatro, Badajoz. He is also regularly called on to write poetry book reviews for several English electronic and paper-based literary journals.

raunchland@hotmail.com

Derek Fyfe

Derek Fyfe is a 48-year-old carer living in Cowdenbeath. At present he is working on his first book of creative memoirs.

drkf@yahoo.co.uk

Sean Howie

Sean Howie was born in 1983, in Dunfermline, Fife. He graduated in 2006 from Goldsmiths University with a BA in English and is currently doing a course in Primary Education. His poem 'Funeral' was written in memory of a friend's father who sadly passed away before his time.

Rachel Marsh

Rachel Marsh has lived in Fife since beginning her MLitt in Creative Writing at the University of St Andrews. After completing the MLitt, she continued to live in St Andrews even though she is now studying for a Postgraduate Research Degree in Scottish Literature at the University of Dundee. Rachel is also Senior Editor of the literary anthology *New Writing Dundee*, teaches creative writing and media studies at Dundee College, and volunteers as an ESOL teacher with Fife Council. Rachel has found the Fife landscape and its people to be a strong and positive influence in her writing.

marshrachel@yahoo.com

Iain Cranford Hunter

Iain Cranford Hunter often paints and draws pictures, and sometimes composes poems. He was born and raised in the west of Fife. He recently moved to Germany. He is 32.

iain@kinzi.co.uk

Amanda Fleet

Amanda Fleet is a physiologist who teaches at St Andrews medical school. In her spare time she writes, enjoys gardening and raises money for a charity in Malawi which she helped to found, that supports street-children back into education. She has lived in Scotland for 16 years.

amanda.fleet@btinternet.com

David Cruickshanks

David Cruickshanks is a local photographer with a passion for writing. He is currently working on his début novel *Fearless* about his experience as a teenage sailor during the Falklands conflict. David is press officer for Fife Veterans association and is married with two rabbits and a Cocker spaniel called Lucy.

Debbie Macdonald

Debbie was born in Fife but spent much of her childhood in Africa and Asia. She left school at 16, and had several jobs before becoming a full-time mother. She then went to university to study mathematics, eventually qualifying as an Actuary. She currently lives in Dunfermline with her husband and children.

Debbie.laird@live.co.uk

Andrew Ferguson

Andrew C. Ferguson is married with one daughter, and lives in Glenrothes. His short fiction has been published in various mainstream and genre magazines, and in various anthologies. A chapbook of Fife football stories is now out from Bloc Press (*www.writers-bloc.org.uk*). Poetry of various kinds has appeared recently or is about to appear in *Chapman, Brand, Iota, Word Salad Magazine, Shantytown Anomaly* and *Farrago's Wainscot.* His poetry pamphlet on the theme of chess,

Head to Head, co-written with Jane McKie, is available from Knucker Press (*www.knuckerpress.com*). More information on forthcoming performances, and some reading samples, are on:

www.myspace.com/andrewcferguson.